VISITING MATTHEW

One Man's Journey through Heaven After Losing a Child

DEAN MORPHONIOS

Scriptures are taken from the King James Bible.
Bible Verses quoted from:
The Holy Bible, King James Version.
Cambridge Edition: 1769

Books may be ordered through booksellers or by contacting:
Dean Morphonios
dean.morphonios@gmail.com
Madison, Florida

ISBN: 978-1-955830-60-7

Printed in the United States of America
Edition Date: June 2022

JESUS SAID:

Revelation 3:20 (KJV) Behold, I stand at the door, and knock: if any man hear my voice, and open the door, I will come in to him, and will sup with him, and he with me.

Matthew 11:28-30 (KJV) Come unto me, all ye that labour and are heavy laden, and I will give you rest. 29 Take my yoke upon you, and learn of me; for I am meek and lowly in heart: and ye shall find rest unto your souls. 30 For my yoke is easy, and my burden is light

DEDICATION

I dedicate "Visiting Matthew" to my Lord and Savior, Jesus Christ, who has blessed me beyond measure and gave me ninety wonderful days in the Fall of 2019 visiting Matthew in Heaven. I present all that I am and all that I ever will be to you, Jesus. Use my life for the benefit of Your Kingdom here on earth and in Heaven above!

I also dedicate "Visiting Matthew" to my beloved son Matthew. Your life was brief and painful. You had a giving heart that easily loved and accepted others. Like all of us, you made mistakes. However, you got one thing right, you chose to accept Jesus as your Lord and Savior when you were nine years old, and for that, I will be forever grateful.

I love you and miss you, Matthew, and I will see you again soon.

I also dedicate this book to my beloved daughter Kimberly Long who has always encouraged me and shared with joy my descriptions of all I was given as I wrote of Heaven. Kimberly, you have a mighty call on your life, and I know I will see the fulfillment of all the Lord has shown me.

I also dedicate this book to my beloved Bride, Mary, who has kept me grounded in Jesus all these years and loves Jesus with every fiber of her being. Mary, thank you for loving me and serving Jesus alongside me all our days!

I also dedicate this book to Judge Andrew and Rosie Decker, who were faithful to spend hours editing my first manuscript and encouraged me to write and publish "Visiting Matthew." Also, to all those unnamed friends who read the manuscript, gave me feedback, and encouraged me. I am forever grateful!

I also dedicate this book to Charles Morris, who lovingly took me under his wings and angelically guided me through the process of publishing. He gave countless hours of his time editing, correcting, and formatting. Charles, you were sent by Heaven to Shepard "Visiting Matthew" to publication. You took a raw jewel of a stone and polished it into an heirloom. I am forever grateful!

Finally, I dedicate "Visiting Matthew" to you, the reader who will walk with me through the passages of Heaven and be an eyewitness to the "Great Battle" for the souls of men. I love each and every one of you with the Love of Jesus. You are the reason that "Visiting Matthew" was written. May you come to know Jesus as your Lord and Savior, fall in love with Him, and serve Him all of your days.

Dean Morphonios
June 2022

CONTENTS

PROLOGUE

In 1995, I attended a little United Methodist Church in Tallahassee, Florida. The church had a tradition of offering the congregation an opportunity each spring to participate in an exercise of faith called "Ten Brave Christians." As a participant, one would agree to dedicate themselves for one month of getting up at 5:30 a.m. to spend one hour with the Lord in prayer and reading His Word, perform a kindness for someone each day, attend church when services are held, and tithe to the church for one month.

At that time, I could not find a way with my bills to tithe, so I chose to do the program on my own I started on the first day of Lent and proposed to discipline myself to do so for the next forty days. Each morning, I read the Book of Matthew and a devotional I had happened upon. I was also reading a book by a retired Catholic Priest that recounted five real-life accounts of Demonic possession. Each day, I would get up at 5:30 a.m., make myself a cup of coffee, and head to the living room for my time with the Lord. The first few days were hard, but then I started really looking forward to that special time with just me and the Lord!

On about the tenth day of my spiritual journey, I had finished the first account of demonic possession by the retired Catholic Priest. Each of the accounts in the book outlined in detailed facts how the person had become possessed and what happened to get them free through the Catholic ritual of exorcism. As I read that first account, I could clearly see how the enemy had attempted to weave his way into my own life to destroy my family and me.

I also clearly saw that those that chose the devil and his ways got precisely what they had sought. Those that chose Jesus received Heaven, and those that failed to make a choice, well, the devil won by default. I was in that latter group, having known from the time that I was a small child that a choice had to be made, but I was holding on to my life, my wife and children, my home, and things. I simply did not want to let go and give all to Jesus. Now, I knew that a choice had to be made.

I also felt a conviction for my own sins that I had never felt before. Little did I know what was about to happen. I just knew that at that moment, I began to weep like a child as I spoke to Jesus, and closing my eyes, I asked Him to forgive me for my sins. I wept and mourned, for I had sinned much. And then I began to give Him everything that I had to give. My dearest treasures on earth, my wife and my two children, as I was praying that prayer, I had a thought pass through my mind that said, "if you go through with this prayer, what you just read, I will do to your daughter."

I hesitated and weighed the cost. I knew that I was about to give everything to Jesus, including my first-born daughter, who I loved more than life itself. I could not think of a better place for her to be protected than with Jesus!

I went forward with my prayer, "Jesus, Forgive me for all my sins. I have sinned against You and Heaven." As I prayed, I felt like I had a claw around my heart, and the claw was opening and lifting. I had my eyes closed, but I could see beyond my closed eyes a bright light, like the sun. I kept praying and spoke.

"I believe and accept that you are The Son of the Living God. You were born of the Virgin Mary and that You died on the Cross for my sins." Now I felt as if something was coming into my heart. It felt like my heart was bigger than I had ever felt, and then the claw was gone. A wonderful and glorious peace like I had never felt before entered my heart. It went through my arms and legs and up and down and through me. I felt that glorious presence of peace radiating from my heart in every direction.

I continued to pray. "That you were buried in a tomb and on the third day you rose from the dead and ascended into Heaven and sit at the right hand of God the Father Almighty." I was now clothed in that glorious presence of something like I had never felt before. "I believe in the Holy Spirit, and I want to be filled with your Holy Spirit. You gave your life for me; I now give my life to you. I will give you everything. Use my life for the benefit of Your Kingdom, here on earth and in Heaven above. I give to you all that I am in Jesus' name!"

When I finished my prayer, I opened my eyes, and there before me was my living room, but now everything seemed different. I felt the glorious presence within me. It was almost like I had been raptured. Gone was a fear that had filled my heart from my earliest remembrance. I went through that first day and went to bed that night, praying that I would feel the same way when I awoke the following day. I awoke to the same glorious presence! By the end of the second day, my wife said to me, "John, you are acting weird. What's going on with you?" I told her all that had happened, and she said, "John, that's the Holy Spirit!" "That's the Holy Spirit?" I asked. I did not know what had happened to me. I was raised in a family that rarely attended church and knew little of the things of God. I was now filled with the Holy Spirit!

I have known much sorrow since that Spring Day in 1995. I had lost my marriage and most of my worldly possessions. My children had experienced trial and tribulation like I would have never imagined, and then I lost my son Matthew to an automobile accident in 2015. However, in all that I suffered, I knew that all was well! My God was faithful! I put my children in His able hands in 1995, and all was well with my soul. The seed of the righteous will not be forsaken! My son Matthew was in Heaven because I chose to give Jesus my life and all I had in 1995.

I would have done it all again a thousand times over, for, on that day in 1995, I found a Pearl of Great Value. I found Jesus! My life and my children's lives and our eternity were secure in Him, for He is faithful to complete the work He began!

The following is a recitation of the imaginations of my heart that the Father revealed to me. It is sincere, and it is based upon the Word of God. The understanding that it brought to me has opened a depth of faith that I had never known before. I have written it in the anointing, which is the threshold test to me whether I am moving with God or outside of Him. Pray over what is revealed, and let the Holy Spirit speak to your heart about the truth of what is revealed.

CHAPTER ONE
DEVASTATING ILLNESS

I had been very sick. Days had blurred into weeks, and I lost sight of time. I knew that my wife and daughter were beside my bed, and my daughter was reading from the Book of Revelation, chapter 21. That was what I used to read when I visited a saint getting ready to leave this life and go on to the next. Was I dying? Somehow, I thought it would be different. I looked up and saw my son Matthew standing beside the bed just next to Kimberly. He looked good, rested, and beaming with the glory of God. But wait, didn't Matthew go on to be with the Lord years ago? I must be having a hallucination. "Come on, dad!" "Matthew, you look so good. I have missed you so much," I said. "Dad, come on," Matthew said again, holding his hand towards me as if to take my hand. He had a smile on his face and a twinkle in his eyes. He had been waiting a long time for this moment, and I could see his excitement.

We had always been close in life. He was so young when he died, just 27 years old, and his death came without announcement. Late for work and driving way too fast, he had lost control and hit a concrete pole. The suddenness of his death had rocked all who knew him but especially his family.

I had cried out the following day asking God to show me that Matthew was all right. Jesus reminded me of nine-year-old Matthew walking the aisle in the little Methodist church and inviting Jesus into his heart. Then Jesus had spoken to my heart, not an audible voice but that still small voice of the Holy Spirit, "Do you believe that Matthew's name was written in the Book of Life?" "Yes, Lord!" I replied. "And it was not removed!" Jesus said to me. Then the peace of God washed over me as Jesus confirmed with His Holy Spirit all that He had told me.

Matthew's passing left a gap for us all, especially for my daughter Kimberly and me. I had always felt in my spirit that when the time came for me to "go home," it would be Matthew that would be sent to lead and comfort me to glory.

"Matthew, I can't go with you. I must be here with Mom and Kimberly. She needs my help." "Dad, Mom, and Kimberly will be just fine without you," Matthew said, still holding out his hand. "Where are we going, Matthew?" I asked. "Do you trust me, dad?" "Of course, I trust you, Matthew!" I said but added, "But where are we going?" "We are going home, dad." "Jesus sent me to lead you home!" "Going home?" I asked. "Yes, dad, we are going home," Matthew responded, smiling at me again with that twinkle in his eyes.

Matthew took me by the hand, and I slipped out of my body like a hand slipping out of a glove. I looked back at my body lying on the bed. I was pale and ashen. Kimberly was crying as she read Revelation 21. She looked up from the Bible and asked, "Daddy? Daddy? Please don't go, daddy!" I looked back at Matthew, and he said, "Come on, dad." "It's all going to be all right!" "But what about Mom and Kimberly," I asked. "Dad, mom will be just fine, and Kimberly will be there to help her," Matthew replied. "Jesus will be with them both, and we will all soon be together, dad." "But you must come with me now and trust Jesus to provide for them," Matthew said. I knew Matthew was right. I knew in my innermost being that it was my time to go home to be with Jesus.

And then we were rising right through the ceiling and into the air higher and higher we went, and it seemed like in a brief second, we came to a beautiful land that I saw in the distance rising from a mist, and then we were there. I had never looked upon anything as beautiful as this land. Everything seemed to shine from within with life. The grass was the greenest grass I had ever seen, soft and velvety. It didn't appear to be mowed. It was grown naturally, and it looked like you would expect a grassy area to look in the 1800s. There were many fir trees, and there was a beautiful crystal-clear river and trees filled with fruit of every kind imaginable for all that lived in that land.

I was wearing a white robe, and so was Matthew. Our robes were alike and were simple and very comfortable. There was a rope-type belt tied around the waist and sleeves that came down to our wrists. I felt drained of energy and weary from our trip to paradise. We sat on a grassy rise looking down at the river, and Matthew reached up to a fruit tree near where we were sitting and pulled the most beautiful pear that I had ever seen from the tree and said, "Here, dad. Try this." The pear was juicy and sweet and tender. It was the most luscious pear that I had ever eaten, and when I ate it, I felt invigorated almost instantly. "Matthew, this is delicious! May I have another?" I asked. Matthew walked over to another tree nearby and brought back a fruit that looked like a peach, sweet and tender, and it too made me feel instantly invigorated. Matthew smiled as he watched me eating the fruit. "How do you feel now, dad? Matthew asked. "Wonderful!" I replied.

CHAPTER TWO
THIS IS HEAVEN

Welcome to Heaven! Matthew said. "This is Heaven?" I asked. "This is Heaven, dad," Matthew answered. "I want to see Jesus," I exclaimed. "He will be here soon, dad," Matthew replied. "How did we get here, Matthew?" I asked.

"Dad, Jesus brought us here." "We live here with Him for eternity." Matthew smiled at me, and his eyes glimmered with joy and amusement as he watched me take in the beauty of Heaven. It was so beautiful, and children were playing nearby, and we could hear their joyful play. Saints walked to and fro, all dressed in the beautiful white robes. Everyone looked young and full of life. Most were following paths that led here, there, and yon. There were many children and some older children and teenagers. Some appeared to be in their early 20s, others were in their late 20s, and some were in their 30s. I never saw anyone older than their 30s.

I wondered how old I looked and Matthew, as if knowing my thoughts, led me to the crystal-clear river with its surface smooth as glass. I looked back at my reflection and saw myself in my late 30s. My hair was long and full again. My eyes sparkled with life, and gone were the wrinkles and age spots that I had gracefully accepted over the last 30 years of my life.

"Matthew, where do we live?" I asked. "I will show you, dad, but not until you have been with the Master. I could feel His presence before I saw Him, but I knew He was there, and as I turned to look, he was walking up to us. How beautiful Jesus is! I could not get over how strikingly beautiful He was. He had a beard and dark brown hair that was full and long, dark brown eyes and thick brown eyebrows, and His eyes, Oh His eyes! More beautiful than anything I had ever seen before or since.

He came to me with His arms outstretched, inviting me, beckoning me to come into His arms, and I ran to Him and fell into His arms! He was wearing a beautiful kingly white robe and a gold sash that flowed from His left shoulder to His right hip. He was taller than my six feet by at least a few inches, and He gently held me back and looked into my tear-washed eyes, and with His right hand, He wiped the tears from my eyes and said, "Welcome home, John!" Oh, what joy, unspeakable and full of glory! He smelled glorious like sweet-cut flowers, and I held Him tightly and wept and wept.

Then He put His arm around me, and we walked side by side as He began to tell me everything and that all was well on the earth. He told me He had strengthened my wife and daughter to accomplish what was required to take care of my burial and do the many things that would have to be done with my homecoming. He told me that the Father was very pleased with me and that we would meet with Him soon. He then explained that He had prepared a place for me and that we would all be together with my family, never to depart from each other again. He told me that Matthew would show me around Heaven and that we would see each other again soon.

Jesus gave me another hug, and I felt the love of God like I had never felt before on earth or in Heaven above. He held out His arms, and Matthew hurried to his arms, and they hugged with such love, and then He walked away. I watched for a long while as He greeted others and walked with the same love, He had shown us. I was enraptured by

His presence and attention, and I did not want Him to go but felt no sadness but only had an inner peace and joy knowing that we would be together forever. I looked over at Matthew, and he was smiling at me, knowing the joy I felt at what I had just experienced and sharing with me my happiness.

"Come on, dad, we've got some special people waiting to see you at home." I walked alongside Matthew as we left the river and walked up a path. Along the way were many beautiful homes that looked more like mansions than homes. I wondered which one we might be turning into, but we kept walking.

Everywhere I looked, I saw people of every color and nation living in perfect harmony, love, and peace. They all seemed so happy and content. We walked through small villages with cobblestone streets that looked like they were on a 1920s movie set. We saw a town square typical of what one might see in the countless little towns in the southern United States. We walked through the countryside with rolling hills, similar to what we see in the Midwest of the United States, and in the distance, I could see mountains rising to great heights.

We walked into the mountains and through a beautiful meadow filled with yellow flowers. Mountain peaks rose from seemingly all sides. Beautiful fir trees and Aspen trees known in the Western mountains of Colorado were all around us. The weather was similar to the most perfect fall day one could ever imagine, with the air soft and dry.

We were in perfect comfort, neither too hot nor cold, and the light of the day glowed about us and did not seem to dim as the day progressed on the earth. I could see no sun but realized that the light that permeated everything seemed to come from a mountain in the far distance. "What is that mountain?" I asked Matthew. "That is the Mountain of God!" Matthew replied. I looked at the mountain, and I could see the glory of God coming from it in every direction. I could not keep my eyes from that mountain. It was the grandest mountain I had ever seen on the earth, and it arose far above all the other mountains that surrounded us.

As we walked through the meadow, I saw deer and antelope grazing. There were many other animals, bears, and mountain lions but all tame. They were perfect specimens and had no fear of our presence but were docile and friendly, walking up to us and allowing us to pet them. I saw a log cabin in the corner of the meadow beside a mountain stream. It looked like the log cabin on the syrup label back on earth, complete with the smoke of a fire burning in the fireplace and the wisp of smoke coming from its chimney that rose from the left side of the cabin. I wondered who was fortunate enough to live there, and then Matthew turned on the path and headed up another way to the cabin.

CHAPTER THREE
A HOME IN HEAVEN

We walked up to the front porch of the cabin. It was a large cabin, one that on earth you would expect to belong to a movie star or someone of means living in Montana or Colorado. There was a large front covered porch with rocking chairs and a porch swing dangling from the rafters above that held the roof to the porch. Matthew led me to the swing, and we sat on it and slowly let it swing back and forth. "Who lives here?" I asked Matthew. "We do," Matthew responded. "This is our cabin?" I asked? "Sure is!" Matthew replied again with that twinkle in his eyes.

Just then, the front door opened, and out walked my beautiful mother. She was in her late twenties and had her hair pulled back from the sides and clipped in back as I remembered seeing a picture of her that had been taken long before I was even born. "Mom," I cried and ran to give her the biggest hug I had ever given anyone in my life! She smiled and hugged me for what seemed like an eternity. I told her how much I had missed her and loved her. She said she had been watching me from Heaven and was anxiously awaiting my coming to be with them. "Come sit with me on the swing." My mother asked, and we sat on the porch swing that Matthew and I had sat upon. The swing was large and could easily hold us. My mother held my hand and looked deeply into my eyes.

"I want to tell you how sorry I am for all the times I made fun of you and called you a Jesus Freak!" "Oh, it's okay, Mom," I responded. "All of that is long since forgiven and forgotten." Well, I want you to know that if you had not pushed through, I would not have been here to greet you. "I know," I replied and then went on to say, "When I fell in love with Jesus in 1995, I was horrified that you and Dale did not know Him, and all I could do was share anything I could get my hands on to try and get you to choose Jesus." "I'm sorry for being overwrought about it." Don't be sorry, John. If you had not been so emphatic, I don't know if I would have said that prayer and been born again."

My mother had been diagnosed with cervical cancer and given six months to live in 2002. During those six months, my wife and I had traveled to her home twice a month to care for mom on the weekends. This care gave my brother and his wife a break from the primary care responsibility. Two years before, when my mother had been in the hospital, I had tried to witness to her and get her to the point of accepting Jesus in her heart. However, when I was sitting with her on her hospital bed and had just begun to explain Isaiah 53, the demons that bound her squeezed, and she burst out with "Shut the Book!" "Shut the Damn Book!" I had been intimidated ever since to approach her with the sinner's prayer. Now that she was given six months to live, I had been sowing seeds of faith in Jesus about every chance I could get. One morning as I was cleaning outside, my wife, Mary, tended and waited on mom and led her in the sinner's prayer. That day, my mother was born again! Praise God!

"Mom, I just knew that Jesus would see that all of us would be together for eternity," I said. "Thank you, John, for not giving up on me and loving me enough to push through, and thank you for loving Jesus as much as you do," My mother replied. "Mom, it was as natural as rain after my Damascus Road experience with Jesus," I said, referring to my conversion.

CHAPTER FOUR
FAMILY IN HEAVEN

Now, as I sat with my beloved mother on that swing in Heaven, looking around at the beautiful mountain scene with the majestic mountains rising all around us and, in the distance, the mountain of God, I was so happy and filled with the wonderful peace of God that permeated Heaven. God's presence was everywhere, and everything glowed with the life of God washed in His glory. My mother looked deep into my eyes, and I saw her as I had never seen her on the earth. Mom was in such a place of peace. Love emanated from her towards me and my love toward her, and we hugged until we were washed again with the glory of God. Matthew, seeming to know the perfect timing, got up from the swing and headed to the front door of the cabin and said, "Come on, dad, I want to show you your new home." Matthew stood at the door, his eyes twinkling with excitement as I allowed my mother to walk before me, and I followed her into my new home.

On earth, I had the idea of having a mansion in Heaven. I had often joked with others about adding another brick to their mansion in Heaven when they did a kindness. Jesus knows the desire of our hearts, and in truth, I love log cabins. I love stone fireplaces and stairways up to the second floor with a large open living area open all the way up to the second story. It would need a banister that one could stand and look over at the stone fireplace below with a warm roaring fire crackling in the fireplace and a large mantle protruding out of the fireplace for pictures of the family.

Visiting Matthew

It was more beautiful than I could have ever imagined. The rich, warm color of the logs with a stone fireplace of river rock that extended up to the ceiling, and it had a large mantle protruding out of the river rock. It had family pictures and a framed portrait of a picture I had loved on earth of the Master sitting in the Garden of Gethsemane overlooking the City of Jerusalem with the Scripture from Matthew 23:37.

Matthew 23:37 (KJV) O Jerusalem, Jerusalem, thou that killest the prophets, and stonest them which are sent unto thee, how often would I have gathered thy children together, even as a hen gathereth her chickens under her wings, and ye would not!

A staircase followed the back wall of the room and led to the upstairs, where there was a log railing overlooking the beautiful living area beneath. There was an open area like what we would consider a kitchen on earth. However, there would be no need for appliances that were so much a part of the American home as there was no need for refrigeration or cooking in Heaven, for there was no decay. There was a large table in the kitchen area where family and friends could sit and break bread together.

Here sat my grandmother and grandfather, both now in their 20s. My grandmother had the most beautiful hair that flowed down to the middle of her back, and my granddaddy had a head full of hair. I jumped for joy and hugged them both. Oh, I was so relieved to see my grandfather as I feared he had never accepted Jesus on the earth as his savior. My grandmother, who seemed to know my thoughts said, "John, don't you remember the picture of Jesus you had for many years that was mine" "Yes, Grandma," I said. "Well, Granddaddy accepted Jesus into his heart during that time when your mother was just a little girl growing up in North Carolina," my grandmother said. As she spoke, my grandfather had tears in his eyes. They both looked so young and full of life and so different than they seemed on earth. We hugged again, and Matthew said, "Come on, dad, and let me show you upstairs."

CHAPTER FIVE
RECONCILED WITH MATTHEW

The cabin was so beautiful, and there were windows everywhere that allowed the beauty of Heaven to come into the cabin. Through every window was a vista that could only be seen on earth in an advertisement for a travel log. Here in Heaven, it was legitimate and true, and I could not fathom the fact that I would never have to leave this beautiful home that Jesus had prepared for me for eternity.

Matthew led us to the stairway, and we ascended to the second floor. We walked past several open doors revealing large bedrooms in the same beautiful warm wood of the cabin with beds and couches with a writing table and chair. He then turned into one of the rooms and said, "This is your room, dad," It was similar to the others we had passed with the warmth and comfort of the rest of the cabin. There was a couch, and two high-back upholstered chairs sat side by side to sit and visit with someone. A large window with a door beside it led to a small porch off the room that looked out over the majestic mountain scene with the Mountain of God in the distance.

"Oh, Matthew, this is just beautiful!" I exclaimed. I started crying tears of joy at all that Jesus had done. At that moment, it seemed any sacrifice I had made on the earth for Jesus paled in comparison to the reward that I now experienced. Jesus is such a good and loving God. He said in His word.

Mark 10:29-31 (KJV) And Jesus answered and said, Verily I say unto you, There is no man that hath left house, or

13

brethren, or sisters, or father, or mother, or wife, or children, or lands, for my sake, and the gospel's, 30 But he shall receive an hundredfold now in this time, houses, and brethren, and sisters, and mothers, and children, and lands, with persecutions; and in the world to come eternal life. 31 But many that are first shall be last; and the last first.

Then Matthew said to me, "Dad, I am so sorry for all the pain I put you through on earth." "It's alright, son," I answered. "No, dad. It is not all right!" Matthew responded! "You see, dad, I knew that you had a mighty call on your life and were meant to do exploits for Jesus. I felt cheated out of my childhood because of your divorce, and I didn't care who I hurt or what pain I caused you or anyone else." "Matthew, I am sorry for all the pain I caused you," I responded. "I did some foolish things that multiplied the pain and suffering you had to live through, and I am so sorry," I said.

We were both crying, cleansing tears of joy as we spoke to each other. There had been so much hurt, and in truth, we had each done things that hurt the other after Matthew's mother, and I divorced. From the perspective of Heaven, it seemed so inconsequential, and yet I knew that it was not, for it led to a place that took both of us off the path we should have been on with Jesus. Satan was behind all of it!

"Matthew, what have you learned about the battle for the souls of men since you came to Heaven?" I asked. "Dad, it is so much worse than people think. It is a daily battle unto death. If people only understood what they were giving up to Satan when they went with his ways instead of the Master's Ways."

Matthew went on to say, "Dad, when I first realized that I was dead from that automobile accident, I left my body and was standing next to the car that was wrapped around that cement pole, and I looked, and an angel was standing beside me. He said to me, "Come on, Matthew, we are going to see Jesus." There were some other creatures that I now know are demons standing there also, and one of them reached out to grab my arm and said, "No, he belongs to us!" I was scared, dad, and that angel knew that I was scared. He said to the demon, "No, I have been sent by the Father, and Matthew's name is written in the Book of Life!" Then that Angel took me by the hand, and we floated up to Heaven. As we left, I saw those demons arguing between themselves, and I could tell they were shocked that they did not have my soul."

"Oh, Matthew, that must have been so frightening," I replied. "It was dad! I had been getting into some horrible stuff, and I had even begun to question whether there was a God at all. It was God's grace that saved me, and God's grace that kept me, and it was grace that brought me home to Heaven," Matthew said. "I was never so thankful than when I looked up and saw that angel." Matthew said and then went on to say, "Dad, if you had not made the choice for Jesus in 1995, I would have never walked that aisle in 1997 and invited Jesus into my heart. It was your commitment to Jesus that gave me the confidence to do the same!" "Thank you, Matthew, for saying that, and I love you, and I am so thankful and grateful to Jesus for letting us be together for eternity," I responded.

"Dad, there is a place here in Heaven that you can go to, and it will transport you to watch any event in the history of God's Kingdom," Matthew began to tell me again with a glimmer of joy in his eyes. "What do you mean? Are you suggesting that in that place, we can actually watch what transpired at that time?" I asked. "That is exactly what I am saying, dad!" Matthew replied. "Have you done this?" I asked. "Sure, that's why I can tell you about it," Matthew replied, smiling.

"Well, what did you experience there?" I asked.

"I wanted to see the crucifixion of our Lord, and I can honestly say that I am so glad I had the opportunity to see firsthand what Jesus suffered for us," Matthew replied. "It was beyond anything that I had ever seen or understood before." "There is no way to express its impact on me. The movies I saw back on earth don't even begin to scratch the surface of the suffering, torment, and pain that Jesus suffered for us," Matthew said.

"How would I go about experiencing that place, Matthew," I asked? "Jesus knows when you are ready, dad, He will come and take you there with Him the first time. After that, you can go anytime you want and experience anything in the history of God's Kingdom," Matthew replied.

"Matthew, would you mind if I rest for a little while? I need some time alone with the Lord." I said, feeling suddenly more tired than I had felt since coming to Heaven. "Sure, dad," Matthew replied. "I am going to my room that is right next to yours towards the stairway. I need to rest, too," Matthew added.

CHAPTER SIX
MY FIRST PRAYER IN HEAVEN

When Matthew left, I went over to the four-post bed made from roughhewn pine that fit the log cabin décor perfectly. I knelt beside the bed and prayed my first prayer in Heaven. "Father, I want you to know how much I love you and Jesus and Your precious Holy Spirit. Thank you, Father, for being such a loving, kind, and compassionate Father. Thank you for making my place in Heaven so wonderful." "I am blessed beyond anything that I could have ever imagined."

It was so wonderful being with Jesus today, and I have never felt Your presence on earth like I have felt it today. I have seen Your glory, and the light of Your glory surrounds me! I am so bathed in your presence that I feel enraptured with every fiber of my being alive with your love and presence.

It was so wonderful seeing Matthew and being with him today. Likewise, It was so wonderful seeing my mother and my grandparents today. I feel such love just enveloping me. I feel Your great love and theirs all wrapped together. I just wanted to thank You before I lay down to rest for a bit, and I want You to know how much I love You! In Jesus' Mighty Name, I pray. Amen."

When I finished, I stayed there quietly on my knees, contemplating all that I had experienced since leaving my body and coming to Heaven, and then I heard God's voice speaking back to me. This sound was an audible voice and not the still small heart voice I often heard on earth. "My son, in whom I am well pleased, I welcome you to your home that was prepared for you from the foundation of the world, and I am with you always." God the Father spoke.

God's voice reverberated and shook my very being. I had just heard the voice of Father God, the God that created the heavens and the earth. I had heard God's voice! I was weeping with joy unspeakable and full of His glory because I had heard God's audible voice! I lay on the bed with a homemade comforter lying on top with my head on pillows and fell fast asleep, vibrating to the core of my being in the presence of God!

I rested for a while and opened my eyes to find myself in my bedroom in Heaven with Jesus sitting in one of the high-back upholstered chairs, smiling at me. "Did you have a good rest?" Jesus asked. "Yes, Lord," I spoke, sitting up in the bed and swinging my feet over, and I was overwhelmed with the sense of love and devotion to our Lord and came quickly to my knees at His feet, worshiping Him. Jesus' feet had a large hole through both feet, and I realized it was the mark of the cross that He bore for eternity.

I felt such love, thankfulness, and devotion to Him for all He did to save me and the world. I wept with tears of joy at being at His feet with total abandoned love. How long I worshiped at Jesus' feet, I could not say. I felt Jesus' hand on my shoulder, and as I looked up, He took my hand and raised me and said, "Come sit here beside me, John," pointing to another high back upholstered chair beside him. The presence of His love was enveloping me, and I was enraptured to be in His presence. I rose and sat in His presence in the chair next to Him.

CHAPTER SEVEN
A VISIT WITH JESUS

How do you like your new home? Jesus asked with a twinkle of joy in his eyes as He saw how joyful I was at all that I had beheld. "Oh, it is all so beautiful, and I cannot stop looking at its beauty!" I replied. "John, you are wondering about the great battle in Heaven that sent Lucifer down to the earth?" Jesus asked. "Yes, Lord," I replied, knowing that God knows our thoughts, and there was no need for me to explain anything that I was contemplating.

It was all over the Father's creation of man. The Father had imagined creating a new being that would be made in His image, unlike the angelic hosts created to serve the Father and His Kingdom. The creation of man was to be subservient only to God but would have dominion over the earth and all that God created on the earth. As an angelic being, Lucifer was going to be required by the Father to serve mankind as he served the Father. That he would not do! He convinced one-third of the angelic hosts to rebel with him against the Father.

Lucifer was specially created by the Father to lead worship, and his very body was a musical instrument, and he was very beautiful. The entire angelic host admired him, and because he was created by the Father to be a leader, he drew at least one-third with him in his plan to overcome the Father and take the Kingdom from Him.

If Lucifer thought he could overthrow God, how did his plan come to light?" I asked Jesus. "The Father knows all things, and He has bound himself to His Word." "There are so many on the earth that fail to understand this fact about the Father," Jesus said.

"Lucifer began to think more of himself than he should have thought. Instead of having a servant's heart, he wanted to be worshiped by all," Jesus continued to say. "He was to serve God, but now he hated the thought of having to serve this puny little man that God desired to create." "Lucifer knew that if he could lay a trap that the Father would step into, he would have him snared, and due to the Father's own desire to stand by His Word, he would overcome the Father and ascend to the throne," Jesus explained.

"He began to discuss his plan with those angelic hosts he believed he could trust to support his rebellion. However, he failed to understand that my father is all-knowing." Jesus explained. "Then there was war in the Heavens." "Do you remember in Revelation 12, John spoke about the war in the Heavens?" Then Jesus began to quote from Revelation 12.

Revelation 12:1 (KJV) And there appeared a great wonder in heaven; a woman clothed with the sun, and the moon under her feet, and upon her head a crown of twelve stars:

Jesus explained that this was His Blessed Mother Mary.

Revelation 12:2 (KJV) And she being with child cried, travailing in birth, and pained to be delivered.

Jesus explained that this was His Birth from Mary.

Revelation 12:3 (KJV) And there appeared another wonder in heaven; and behold a great red dragon, having seven heads and ten horns, and seven crowns upon his heads.

Jesus explained that this was Satan.

Revelation 12:4 (KJV) And his tail drew the third part of the stars of heaven, and did cast them to the earth: and the dragon stood before the woman which was ready to be delivered, for to devour her child as soon as it was born.

Jesus explained that the third part of the stars of heaven that were cast to the earth was the one-third of the angelic hosts that rebelled against God and joined Lucifer's rebellion) (the effort to devour the child was when Satan led Herod to kill all of the male children two years or younger in Bethlehem.

Revelation 12:5 (KJV) And she brought forth a man child, who was to rule all nations with a rod of iron: and her child was caught up unto God, and to his throne.

Jesus explained that He was the child.

Revelation 12:6 (KJV) And the woman fled into the wilderness, where she hath a place prepared of God, that they should feed her there a thousand two hundred and threescore days.

Jesus explained that this represented his escape into Egypt for three and ½ years.

Revelation 12:7 (KJV) And there was war in heaven: Michael and his angels fought against the dragon; and the dragon fought and his angels,

Jesus explained that the actual war was long before he was born from the Virgin Mary.

Revelation 12:8 (KJV) And prevailed not; neither was their place found any more in heaven.

Revelation 12:9 (KJV) And the great dragon was cast out, that old serpent, called the Devil, and Satan, which deceiveth the whole world: he was cast out into the earth, and his angels were cast out with him.

Jesus explained that this occurred before the creation of man.

"John, I want to take you on a trip with me to the city." "What city, Lord?" I asked. "Jerusalem! Have you not read that the streets are paved with gold in Heaven?" Jesus asked, smiling as he spoke and with a twinkle in his eyes and then quoted from Revelation 21:21:

Revelation 21:21 (KJV) And the twelve gates were twelve pearls; every several gate was of one pearl: and the street of the city was pure gold, as it were transparent glass.

"Yes, Lord. I do remember that in the Word of God. I believe it was in the Book of Revelation." I replied. "That's right, John. We are going to the mountain of God, and there we will find Jerusalem, a city with streets of gold. We will also find a special place that the Father has provided for His children to go and learn about the history of the Kingdom of God by experiencing it firsthand," Jesus said. "Matthew was just telling me about that place, Lord, and I so want to go and experience it," I replied.

CHAPTER EIGHT
MY FIRST VISIT IN HEAVENLY JERUSALEM: THE TIME PORTAL

I began to get up to go out with Jesus, and as I started to get up, Jesus held up His hand, signaling me to sit back down. "We will go from here, John," Jesus spoke. "How Lord?" I asked. Jesus held out His left hand, and when I took it, we were suddenly walking on a street of gold. It was transparent gold so pure that you could look within it. It shined and reflected, and it was broad like a six-lane highway back on earth.

Jesus and I walked side by side. Saints were walking all around us, and they wore the white robes of righteousness like I was wearing. Jesus smiled at them as we walked and knew each one intimately as He knew me. They all smiled at us and would have gladly fellowshipped with us but seemed to know that Jesus was leading me someplace and respectfully restrained themselves.

On both sides of the street were shops and beautiful landscaped parks, and there were also, at times, homes that were like the homes that lined streets in the Victorian era of America. These homes were quaint and appeared to be two-story. Trees of various types lined the street; some were fruit trees like we had passed earlier when Matthew first escorted me through Heaven.

Up ahead, the street seemed to divide with half going to the right and half going to the left around a large crystal-type building set apart in that place. The building was also beautifully landscaped and was multi-storied. As we approached it, we could see saints in various locations within the building standing around a pedestal with their hands on something on the pedestal.

The entry to the building was a revolving door, and Jesus and I entered together and pushed the door to the place where we stepped into the building. We were in a lobby, and I saw angels helping the saints and directing them to certain pedestals within the building. Because the entire building was glass, one could always see outside the building and see the saints walking to and fro, moving about Heaven.

One of the angels approached Jesus and me and reverently spoke to Jesus. He was of medium build, about 5'10", with long flowing brown hair. He had a face that was pleasant to look upon with brown eyebrows, brown eyes, and a quick smile. He was wearing a robe of white, and you could see wings that were folded back that went down his back from above his head to the back of his knees. "Master, is there something I can help You and John with?"

I was surprised that he knew my name. Jesus said, "Yes, Andrew, would you show John to the portal that depicts Lucifer and the Fall of Man?" Jesus asked. "Yes. Certainly Master," the angel responded. Jesus then turned to me and said that He had to go but that Matthew would soon be coming along to show me back home.

I hugged Jesus and wanted to hold on to Him for about a million years but respectfully released my hug, and He looked me in the eyes and said, "I love you, John." "I love you so much, Jesus!" I responded. He looked me in the eyes, smiled, and turned to walk out the way we had come into the building. I watched as Jesus exited the building, and people near came to Him and hugged Him as He lovingly hugged them back. There was such joy on the faces of all the people and Jesus.

Andrew led me to a pedestal in a room (also made of glass), and there I saw a gold dome that protruded from the top of the pedestal. Andrew told me to simply place my hand on the dome, and I would be transported to watch whatever event in the history of God's kingdom that I desired to experience. I thanked Andrew and said, "Andrew, may I ask you a question?" I asked.

"Certainly, John," Andrew responded. "Andrew, what was it like for you when you saw Lucifer drawing together some of your own brethren and moving to rebel against God?" I asked. Andrew hesitated, looked down, and then back to me, looking into my eyes, "John, Lucifer was as beguiling to my brethren as he was to man. I was kept only by my great love for the Father, the Son, and the Holy Ghost. I was not beguiled," He said and said no more. "Let me know if there is anything more I can do to help," Andrew said and then turned and walked away.

I stood looking at the pedestal, and with my right hand, I placed it upon the gold dome. Instantly, I was transported.

Dean Morphonios

CHAPTER NINE
LUCIFER:
THE ARCHANGEL OF WORSHIP

I saw God's throne, and it was high and lifted up, and there was a river of fire that surrounded the throne. I could hear the most beautiful chorus of angels singing in unison the most beautiful song of praise to God. I saw one of the angels, and he was producing the most beautiful music, and it seemed that it was coming from his own body. He was such a beautiful angel in every way, so beautiful that there was not anything about him that was not beautiful. He was completely beautiful. He seemed to sparkle like jewels sparkle in a jewelry store glass case with lights shining down upon them from above. As he produced the music, the sea of angels was in unison with the music produced by this one angel. Somehow, I knew that this was Lucifer and remembered the Scripture from Ezekiel 28.

Ezekiel 28:13-15 (KJV) Thou hast been in Eden the garden of God; every precious stone was thy covering, the sardius, topaz, and the diamond, the beryl, the onyx, and the jasper, the sapphire, the emerald, and the carbuncle, and gold: the workmanship of thy tabrets and of thy pipes was prepared in thee in the day that thou wast created. 14 Thou art the anointed cherub that covereth; and I have set thee so: thou wast upon the holy mountain of God; thou hast walked up and down in the midst of the stones of fire. 15 Thou wast perfect in thy ways from the day that thou wast created, till iniquity was found in thee.

26

Visiting Matthew

I saw God the Father sitting on a throne, and on His right hand was Jesus, His Son, and He was the smitten image of His Father. Before the Father was a sea of angels. I could see a hierarchy among the angels, and the greatest of them was grander than any of the others. These angels were right at the Throne, and they surrounded the Throne. All the other angels were far back from these that surrounded the Throne.

I knew in my spirit that I was looking upon the archangels of which I remembered that Michael and Gabriel were archangels. All the angels were dressed in a similar dress of white robes. Likewise, all had wings that came out of their back and rose above their head, reaching down as far as the back of the lower legs. The archangels were dressed in white robes also but had a banner of honor that distinguished them from the other angels. The archangels also had a presence about them, and one was drawn to them as they seemed to have a level of authority about them that one could not deny, and each of them had a throne.

CHAPTER TEN
ANGER AND PRIDE:
THE REBELLION OF LUCIFER

All of the angels were gathered around the throne, and it was clear that The Father was about to reveal something remarkable that He wanted to speak to them about. Soon the music from Lucifer, the angel producing it, began to wane, and soon every eye of the angels was upon the Father.

I did not see men or women before the throne as this seemed to be before the creation of man. The Father began to speak, and I could hear His voice reverberating through the great hall. His language was different from anything I had ever heard before, but somehow, I understood what he was saying. As he spoke, I could see God creating an image that seemed to be before the angels, not on a screen but above them and before them, and it was like the vision floated in the air.

I saw God describe His vision to them of His creation of a man and woman that would be made in His image and likeness. I could see the countenance of Lucifer, the angel that was leading the worship, and as God described the man and the women, his countenance began to change. I could see that he contained himself but seemed to have pride and anger that were building within him. There were many other angels in the sea of angels. I could see their eyes upon this angel leading the worship, and their countenance also changed with the archangel as they cast their eyes upon him and each other.

Other angels seemed to be enthralled at what God was describing about the man and woman He was going to create. It was so exciting to most of the angels because God would create man "In His Image." He was God Almighty and had created each one of the angels. They were designed to serve Him, and they each had a wonderful life serving God, Jesus, and the Holy Spirit in Heavenly realms. However, they were not robots, but each was created with free will. Now, they would be called upon to serve this new creation God called man. They had never heard or conceived that God would create a being in His own image. After all, He was God Almighty, and nothing compared or came close to His grandeur or His glory and power and might.

Although God was telling them that he would create man in His image, man would be placed on the planet that God had created called earth. All the angels had been wondering what God would do with earth.

CHAPTER ELEVEN
GOD REVEALS HIS PLAN FOR MANKIND

God had created an oasis of a planet when He created the earth. God created it in the midst of nothingness, speaking it into existence. It reflected His glory in all that he created. While creating the planet earth, God had created an unimaginable universe of stars, planets, and galaxies and had uniquely placed the earth in such a position so that when He made the stars, planets, and galaxies around the planet, it was in a perfect position.

God had also made the earth self-promulgating and created oceans, land, plants, grasses, trees, fish of the sea, and animals of the land, all self-promulgating. He created the atmosphere around the earth to provide the air and nurturing water that His creation of life would need to survive. He created the plants to create the nurturing air that filled the atmosphere and provided for life. It was a perfect, balanced ecological system in every respect. All and all, the earth was a wonderful creation, and speculation was very high as to what God would do with this jewel of His designs.

And now God was telling them about His plan to create a man in His own image. Although created in the image of God, man would have a body that existed in the physical realm of the earth and not the spiritual kingdom of Heaven. The man would also have a spirit and thus would have eternal life. In essence, man would be a spirit being but would exist in a physical body in the world of the earth. The angels would be expected to serve mankind but invisible to them, being spirit beings unless God granted them to appear for some purpose.

God said He created man for His own pleasure to have fellowship with him. God said that man would have dominion over the earth and be submissive only to Him and that the man would be above the angels who would again be required to serve God first and then the man He created.

Lucifer's countenance changed as the Father spoke of His creation. I could tell that the notion of God having fellowship with this created being called "Man" was causing Lucifer to rise in pride. More anger began to show on his face. In the light of the glory of Heaven, it appeared to be a darkness that crossed over his face with his eyebrows forced downward.

God would give man complete choice, as he was created in God's image, to either love Him or not. God would honor man's will and allow a choice to be made. God would place within the midst of a Garden where the man would reside two trees, the tree of Life and the Tree of Knowledge of Good and Evil.

God said He would forbid the man from eating from the Tree of Knowledge of Good and Evil but give him all the other trees in the garden to have as he desired. Should the man take from the Tree of Knowledge of Good and Evil, he would violate God's Word, and his lack of obedience would show a lack of love for God. This disobedience would, in turn, result in the wounding of his fellowship with God.

CHAPTER TWELVE
WAR IN HEAVEN

After God left the throne, the angels began to mill around, discussing what had just transpired. They were all speculating on what the man would be like and how it would all come to pass. But as for Lucifer, I could see that he was all business. As he moved about speaking conspiratorially to other angels, his countenance was disturbed, as were the other angels that he spoke to. I thought of the Scripture from Genesis 4.

Genesis 4:6-7 (KJV) And the LORD said unto Cain, Why art thou wroth? and why is thy countenance fallen? 7 If thou doest well, shalt thou not be accepted? and if thou doest not well, sin lieth at the door. And unto thee shall be his desire, and thou shalt rule over him.

I could sense that sin was lying at Lucifer's door. There was so much of the Love of God in Heaven, and it permeated everything. As I looked upon Lucifer and his angels, I felt an awful feeling of hatred. There had been times on the earth when I had experienced evil, but in my short time in the Paradise of Heaven, I had forgotten how horrible that feeling was.

I saw Lucifer speaking to a group of angels who were enthralled at what he was saying to them. I could hear him saying to them. "Who is this man that we are to serve?" Lucifer continued speaking to the other angels. "We have existed for eons serving God, and we should have a greater place than to have to serve this nothing creation that, on a whim, God decides He is going to create in His own image to have fellowship? If I were God, I would reward those angels that had served me so well with thrones, and they would be honored, and never would I ask them to serve this thing called man. Instead, I would have this puny slime of a man serve us!"

I could not imagine that this was going on in Heaven, that there, in God's own paradise, such betrayal was happening. Right there in Heaven. It hurt my heart to see it because of my love for my Father. I have heard it said that love and hate are very similar and that love can quickly turn into hate. I know that mankind is capable of both emotions, both being extreme on the emotional scale but on opposite ends of the scale. I knew little about angels. I knew they had free will and could decide to obey or disobey. But did they have emotions also? Could they love and hate? I observed Lucifer choosing to hate, and as I saw his choice manifest, I also saw his countenance change from beautiful to ugly.

I could feel the tension as the evil darkness spread among the angels that aligned themselves with Lucifer. I was aware of the scripture from Revelation 12.

Revelation 12:7 (KJV) And there was war in heaven: Michael and his angels fought against the dragon; and the dragon fought and his angels,

I wondered how the war was fought in Heaven. The angels I witnessed were spirit beings. How would spirit beings war against each other? I thought about my life on earth. How did demons fight against me to stop the will of God from going forward in my own life on earth? I realized that much of the battle was fought in my mind and emotions, with the demonic dropping thoughts and visions in my mind tempting me to sin against the Lord. I thought about how they used the flesh of other people to bring offenses. I thought about Satan causing people to have offenses against me and then trying to put offenses and judgment in me against them.

The angels would equally fight against the demonic warfare to cause God's people to prevail by moving in Faith in God's Word. When God's people spoke, stood, and obeyed God's Word, the angels would be empowered to bring it to pass.

I knew that God was aware of all things as He is omniscient. As I watched the conspiratorial actions of Lucifer and his contingent of angels that had aligned themselves to his cause against God, I saw a more significant number of angels that were faithful to God bringing themselves in a unified attack against Lucifer and his angels. I realized that Lucifer and the angels that conspired with him had committed iniquity by thinking, speaking, and acting against God and His Kingdom. I remembered what God said through his prophet Ezekiel.

Ezekiel 28:15-18 (KJV) Thou wast perfect in thy ways from the day that thou wast created, till iniquity was found in thee. 16 By the multitude of thy merchandise they have filled the midst of thee with violence, and thou hast sinned: therefore I will cast thee as profane out of the mountain of God: and I will destroy thee, O covering cherub, from the midst of the stones of fire. 17 Thine heart was lifted up because of thy beauty, thou hast corrupted thy wisdom by reason of thy brightness: I will cast thee to the ground, I will lay thee before kings, that they may behold thee. 18 Thou hast defiled thy sanctuaries by the multitude of thine iniquities, by the iniquity of thy traffick; therefore will I bring forth a fire from the midst of thee, it shall devour thee, and I will bring thee to ashes upon the earth in the sight of all them that behold thee.

CHAPTER THIRTEEN
LUCIFER AND HIS ANGELS CAST FROM HEAVEN

I saw the angels of Lucifer attempting to persuade the other angels to join them in their mutiny against God. I saw many of God's angels immediately shut them down by rebuking them for their rebellion, lifting their love for God, and declaring their loyalty and allegiance to the Almighty God.

I realized how wonderful it was for God to see the faithfulness of His angels and how hurtful it must have been to God's heart to see the rebellion take place. Clearly, the majority of the angels were standing with God, and I knew that this was causing a division in the camp of angels that numbered in the millions. The angels that had decided with Lucifer were themselves changing in their countenance. It was as if they did not understand what was happening within themselves, as if they had been deceived and were unaware of it.

As a man looking upon this battle, I felt the emotions of the negativity but also the emotions of the faithfulness in those angels that stood with the Lord. I felt great comfort in knowing their stand for God and His righteous ways. I did not see shields and swords in the hands of the angels. I saw an angel that I knew to be Michael and saw that he was getting hit with unimaginable blasphemy against the Lord that was being spoken into his mind. I also saw him hit with the emotions of the attack and knew that angels did feel emotions like men, such as fear, doubt, and unbelief. I saw him flinch at the power of the attack, and I knew and could even feel the mind-binding attack in my own mind as I watched the warfare in Heaven.

All of the Lord's angels were equally struggling against the strength of this mind-binding attack, but they all stood strong for the Lord. They spoke God's Word as a sword against what Lucifer and his angels were saying against the Lord. They defended God using His Word showing that God is faithful and true! They stood strong in His faithfulness and His love.

I could not keep up with the blasphemies Lucifer and his fallen angels were saying against God our Father, Jesus, and His Holy Spirit. They were unimaginable blasphemies, and I recognized the author of cussing and a foul mouth was nothing less than Satan himself. It was consistent with the level of darkness that Lucifer and his angels had dropped to in their rebellion against God.

I also recognized many verses that the angels for the Lord would speak back during the attack. I realized what comfort the Word of God was to our stand with God against the powers of darkness.

1 John 3:24 (KJV) And he that keepeth his commandments dwelleth in him, and he in him. And hereby we know that he abideth in us, by the Spirit which he hath given us.

John 14:15 (KJV) If ye love me, keep my commandments.

Proverbs 21:21 (KJV) He that followeth after righteousness and mercy findeth life, righteousness, and honour.

Deuteronomy 7:9 (KJV) Know therefore that the LORD thy God, he is God, the faithful God, which keepeth covenant and mercy with them that love him and keep his commandments to a thousand generations;

Matthew 22:37-40 (KJV) Jesus said unto him, Thou shalt love the Lord thy God with all thy heart, and with all thy soul, and with all thy mind. 38 This is the first and great commandment. 39 And the second is like unto it, Thou shalt love thy neighbour as thyself. 40 On these two commandments hang all the law and the prophets.

I could not believe the wicked and evil things that Lucifer and his angels were saying against the Lord, and I again felt the mind-binding effect of those evil words spoken by them. However, as Michael and the other angels of the Lord spoke, I could feel the presence of the Lord being magnified, and the power of God began to push back the evil darkness of Lucifer and his angels.

As the battle progressed, Lucifer and his angels changed before my eyes. Gone was the glory of God from their countenance, and as the hate of God grew in Lucifer and his angels, I saw their brightness dim, and their appearance was of death itself. Love was turned into hatred. Beauty was turned into ugliness. The light was turned into darkness. The glory of God left Lucifer and his angels. Then, most dramatically, I heard God speak, and His voice thundered through Heaven as I watched a fire begin within Lucifer, and it spread all over him and his angels, and then he and one-third of the angelic hosts were cast from Heaven to the earth. It was like some tremendous magnetic force grabbed at them, and they were yanked from Heaven and violently cast down upon the earth:

Revelation 12:7-9 (KJV) And there was war in heaven: Michael and his angels fought against the dragon; and the dragon fought and his angels, 8 And prevailed not; neither was their place found any more in heaven. 9 And the great dragon was cast out, that old serpent, called the Devil, and Satan, which deceiveth the whole world: he was cast out into the earth, and his angels were cast out with him.

CHAPTER FOURTEEN
THE WORD OF GOD DEFEATS SATAN

W hen they were gone, the angels of God responded with praise for God and began to worship Him in Spirit and truth. The love of God filled Heaven once again. Gone forever was the strife and evil that had permeated God's Heavenly paradise. Soon, God and His Son Jesus came back to their throne, and all His faithful angels bowed and worshiped God Almighty, proclaiming His Omnipotence, saying:

Revelation 19:6 (KJV) And I heard as it were the voice of a great multitude, and as the voice of many waters, and as the voice of mighty thunderings, saying, Alleluia: for the Lord God omnipotent reigneth.

Revelation 4:11 (KJV) Thou art worthy, O Lord, to receive glory and honour and power: for thou hast created all things, and for thy pleasure they are and were created.

Revelation 5:12-13 (KJV) Saying with a loud voice, Worthy is the Lamb that was slain to receive power, and riches, and wisdom, and strength, and honour, and glory, and blessing. 13 And every creature which is in heaven, and on the earth, and under the earth, and such as are in the sea, and all that are in them, heard I saying, Blessing, and honour, and glory, and power, be unto him that sitteth upon the throne, and unto the Lamb for ever and ever.

I wondered about how I observed the war fought in Heaven, and I thought about how the angels of the Lord used the word of God to fight Lucifer and his angels. I also thought of how Jesus had used the word of God to fight Satan in the wilderness when He responded to each temptation with "It is written." I realized what God had said in the Book of John, chapter 1.

John 1:1-3 (KJV) In the beginning was the Word, and the Word was with God, and the Word was God. 2 The same was in the beginning with God. 3 All things were made by him; and without him was not any thing made that was made.

John 1:14 (KJV) And the Word was made flesh, and dwelt among us, (and we beheld his glory, the glory as of the only begotten of the Father,) full of grace and truth.

Jesus is the Word made flesh, and time exists outside of God. What I had just observed were the holy angels of God using the Word of God that had not yet been written in the course of time. I realized that the Word was written from the beginning of time and only came to be in the course of time to bring forth all that God said would happen. God had already proclaimed it before it happened. Jesus was the Word made flesh. I realized how vitally important the Word of God was to mankind and how in life, I had failed to realize its truth, faithfulness, and power. In truth, God is faithful to His Word and will bring it to pass if spoken by men with faith.

Now, Satan had been cast down to the earth. He had been defeated in this great battle in Heaven by the Word of God.

Isaiah 14:9-21 (KJV) Hell from beneath is moved for thee to meet thee at thy coming: it stirreth up the dead for thee, even all the chief ones of the earth; it hath raised up from their thrones all the kings of the nations. 10 All they shall speak and say unto thee, Art thou also become weak as we? art thou become like unto us? 11 Thy pomp is brought down to the grave, and the noise of thy viols: the worm is spread under thee, and the worms cover thee. 12 How art thou fallen from heaven, O Lucifer, son of the morning! how art thou cut down to the ground, which didst weaken the nations! 13 For thou hast said in thine heart, I will ascend into heaven, I will exalt my throne above the stars of God: I will sit also upon the mount of the congregation, in the sides of the north: 14 I will ascend above the heights of the clouds; I will be like the most High. 15 Yet thou shalt be brought down to hell, to the sides of the pit. 16 They that see thee shall narrowly look upon thee, and consider thee, saying, Is this the man that made the earth to tremble, that did shake kingdoms; 17 That made the world as a wilderness, and destroyed the cities thereof; that opened not the house of his prisoners? 18 All the kings of the nations, even all of them, lie in glory, every one in his own house. 19 But thou art cast out of thy grave like an abominable branch, and as the raiment of those that are slain, thrust through with a sword, that go down to the stones of the pit; as a carcase trodden under feet. 20 Thou shalt not be joined with them in burial, because thou hast destroyed thy land, and slain thy people: the seed of evildoers shall never be renowned. 21 Prepare slaughter for his children for the iniquity of their fathers; that they do not rise, nor possess the land, nor fill the face of the world with cities.

I had seen it happen. I saw Satan cast out of Heaven, he and his angels down to the earth. I was shaking to the core of my being, having witnessed this great event in the history of God's Kingdom. I suddenly felt overwhelmed with it all and knew that I needed to go back to the cabin and rest before I continued on this journey of witnessing the creation and fall of man in the garden.

CHAPTER FIFTEEN
THE GREAT PORTAL OF HEAVEN

With that thought, I found myself back at the podium in the crystal building in Heaven as I was withdrawing my hand from the gold dome at the top of the podium. As I became aware of my surroundings once again, I saw Matthew outside, walking among the saints and coming to the entrance to the building. I turned, and Andrew was there with his hand on my shoulder, encouraging me. He had a look of compassion in his eyes, and he spoke to me, saying, "It's all right, John, what you have witnessed today is not an easy thing to see." "Thank you, Andrew," I replied. "Go with Matthew and rest," Andrew suggested, "and you come back when you feel up to it, and we will continue your journey." "Thank you, Andrew," I replied a second time and looked up to see Matthew smiling as he came up to Andrew and me.

"I just can't get used to seeing my dad in Heaven!" Matthew said, smiling with that twinkle in his eyes again. "Jesus said you would be escorting me back to the cabin," I said to Matthew. "And I will give you a tour of Heaven on the way back," Matthew said.

We walked together outside the glass building again using the revolving door. Matthew said when we got outside, "Come on, dad! I have to show you this little park where I like to come and sit and meditate on the goodness of God." As we walked together to the park, we passed saints, and it seemed like everybody in Heaven knew us by name. "Hi, John!" "Hi, Matthew!" I wondered again how everybody knew me.

Visiting Matthew

"How do they know my name, Matthew?" I asked. "They have been watching the great battle over the banister of Heaven, dad," Matthew responded. "Really?" I asked. "Sure!" Matthew responded. "Do you want to see it?" "Yes, Matthew," I replied. Matthew then led me to another building that was circular-shaped with a large circular dome. It was called by all in Heaven the Great Portal of Heaven. I was reminded of the great aquariums that I had seen on earth, where people entered them and could see the fish swimming beneath the water as if they were right there under the water with them. Those aquariums on earth were always darkened on the inside. The light of the enormous tank of water would enter through the large windows, while people would stand and gaze at the underwater fish.

I had always thought about the saints "looking over the banister of Heaven" and had imagined a real banister with saints looking over it and supernaturally seeing their loved ones on the earth. They could watch the goings-on with the natural and the supernatural. But what I was about to see would alter that impression forever!

CHAPTER SIXTEEN
LOOKING BACK ON THE EARTH FROM HEAVEN

We walked into the building from the street level, and I was immediately stunned and taken back. What I saw was huge! I saw the earth suspended in space right before us, complete with its atmosphere of clouds and storms, and the earth was moving as it appeared in space. One could see that it had one side facing light, and the other side was darkened with night. It was larger than anything I could imagine, and around the globe of the earth was a banister. Saints were standing looking at the earth, and somehow, they were experiencing the supernatural experience of viewing their family and friends from the vantage point of the banister.

Once again, an angel greeted us by name. "Matthew, it is so good to see you again." "Thank you, Joseph," Matthew replied. "Have you met my dad?" "Hello, John," the angel spoke directly to me. "How have you enjoyed your new home?" "Oh, it is more wonderful than I could have ever imagined," I responded with joy smiling. "Would you like to see over the banister of Heaven today at your family?" Joseph asked us. "Yes, please," Matthew responded.

The angel led us to a place on the banister that overlooked the earth. The globe continued to turn in front of us, and I thought about how different it looked from space. I thought how odd it was that the Southern United States, where I had resided with my wife and family, was much farther up on the globe of the earth than I would have thought. Matthew told me to simply look, and we would be able to see.

Suddenly, we were visually transported to the earth. I realized that we were still standing in Heaven but were permitted to experience the existence on earth at that time and place as if we were there. I saw my wife sitting next to my daughter, and they were in an office discussing the arrangements for the funeral they were planning for me.

My daughter was holding my wife's hand, and my wife was telling the funeral director what music she wanted to be played in the background of my service scheduled for two days hence. Both my wife and daughter looked like they had not had an hour's worth of sleep. They looked exhausted. The funeral director discussed the bill with them, and I saw my daughter reach into her purse, pull out a checkbook, and write a check to the director.

I felt terrible watching them because I knew that they were both very weary and appeared almost in a state of shock. I saw the Holy Spirit within them, and I could see the Holy Spirit's presence extending from both my wife and daughter and permeating the room they were sitting within. I saw that two large angels were standing guard on either side of them, and another one was at the funeral director's office door.

The funeral director was very pious and managed his smiles and emotions carefully so as not to seem too joyful nor too glum. The director did not have any presence of the Holy Spirit around him, and he looked dull compared to the glowing presence of my wife and daughter. I could see a demon leering out from behind his eyes, and I knew that he did not know Jesus. How odd because he seemed to know exactly what my wife was saying to him as if he were a true believer, and I realized that the director was playing a role.

He would adjust the role for whoever was sitting before him so that he could be all things to all people.

I watched my wife and daughter walk out of the office, and then my wife turned and asked the funeral director if she could see me. He looked uncomfortable and gave reasons why that would not be proper as they had not prepared my body for the service. I knew my wife, and I could tell that she was persistent. However, the funeral director was equally so, and so she finally turned, and with my daughter's encouragement, they walked from the office.

We watched them get into my daughter's car and drive back to my house. When they pulled into the garage, my wife explained to my daughter that she needed to rest, and she went to our room. I could see that an angel accompanied her wherever she went. As she entered the house, praise music played that my wife and I always played continually within our home. I could see the holiness of our home compared with the meeting that had just taken place with the funeral director.

My wife went into our bedroom and lay on the bed. I saw her weep uncontrollably for a few minutes. Then she began praying to Jesus about how much she was hurting. Then she spoke her faith and belief that all was well in Heaven where I was with Jesus and asked Him to strengthen her and my daughter to rise to all that needed to be done over the next few days. I saw as she prayed that the glory of God began to thicken around her, and soon she was enveloped in that glory and fell fast asleep.

CHAPTER SEVENTEEN
A DEMON OF GRIEF DEFEATED

I had often sensed the anointing when I was on the earth and would use it to guide me in all that I did each day. Now, in the Heavenly glory, I watched the battle being fought around my wife, and I could see a demon of grief lurking around, seeking to influence her as she wept on the bed. He would wave his hands at her, and I saw the darkness of the grief descend over her as she lay in the bed. Then as my wife prayed, I watched as she began speaking truth from the Word of God. The angel standing beside her bed began to fan the glory of the Lord. As the glory flowed into the room and moved towards that demon, he cringed and shrank back into a corner. He was a monkey-looking creature that was small and ugly. He had dirtiness about him, and I could only imagine how bad he must have smelled.

I could see my daughter sitting at the kitchen table. She was on the phone with her husband, and she, too, was crying and inconsolable. I wanted to take her tears, for if she only knew that I was right here beside Matthew, she would feel no grief. I could see another demon of grief sitting next to her at the table. He looked much like the other demon, a small monkey-looking creature that was ugly and dirty. He acted much like the other demon did with my wife doing everything he could to bring my daughter into greater grief.

My daughter was very close to the Lord, as was my wife, and she knew a great deal about the things of the Kingdom of God. She finished her call and went to battle. I saw her stand up from the table, and she began to do some serious demon butt-kicking! I was so blessed to see her go to war!

She started by declaring the Word of God. "Death, where is your sting and grave, where is your victory? Then she proclaimed who I was in Christ, that I was in Heaven because I had accepted the gift of salvation when I was 39 years old, and that I had been born again. She proclaimed that to be absent from the body was to be present with the Lord and that we would see each other again. She took authority over the spirit of grief, and I saw the demon sitting beside her at the table begin to tremble, and noticeable fear appeared in him.

My daughter then spoke with authority, "you foul spirit of grief, you have no place here because you were defeated 2000 years ago when Jesus Christ, the Son of the living God, died on the cross for my dad's sins and my sins and He paid the price for my dad's salvation. Jesus Christ took the keys of death, hell, and the grave. He defeated Satan and redeemed us. You can't be redeemed, you foul spirit of death and grief, and your future is a lake of fire (that demon was paralyzed with fear now), for every knee shall bow and confess that Jesus Christ is Lord!"

Then my daughter specifically took authority and bound that spirit of grief, muzzled it into silence, and cast it out into the abyss, never returning until the Day of Judgment. I saw that demon spirit yanked out of the chair, and he was sucked by an unseen force into the earth and was instantly gone. My daughter continued by declaring, "I loose the power of the Holy Spirit, mighty warrior angels, and the precious blood of our Lord and Savior Jesus Christ to cover, protect and deliver."

I could see the glory of God descend into the kitchen, and the presence of the Holy Spirit intensified. I could see angels come into the kitchen, and they provided an angel guard around my daughter. I could see that my daughter had God's peace come over her. My daughter picked up her Bible, sat back down at the table, and began to read Psalm 34, and I could see that she was comforted and at peace!

CHAPTER EIGHTEEN
EXPLORING HEAVEN

I turned and looked at Matthew and said, "Matthew, I think we ought to go." "Sure, Dad," Matthew responded, and we turned and walked back to the door of the Great Portal of Heaven building. As we walked outside, Matthew asked me, "Are you okay, dad?" "I am fine, Matthew," I responded, "I guess I had lost sight of the struggles on the earth being in Heaven with all of the glory of God around us." "I know," Matthew responded. "I remember my first trip to the Great Portal of Heaven, and I had a similar experience!"

In Heaven, I felt no sadness but seeing the pain and suffering of my wife and daughter were hard because I wanted them to be able to look through the portal and see how well things were for me in Heaven. I wanted my daughter to see and know that I was all right. But I also knew they would have to rely upon their faith to see, and I knew they were strong in his faith. I knew they would fall back on Jesus to strengthen and carry them through.

As we walked on those streets of gold in Heaven, we passed many saints. They were all so happy and kind, smiling or waving and acknowledging our presence with gladness. I was reminded of the small Christian school I attended in Miami, Florida, growing up. I had been torn about going to the Christian school one year and asked my mother to withdraw me and let me go to the public school. I was about 15 years old at that time. I found out quickly how cold and threatening the outside world was to the comfort of the little cocoon of that Christian school that only had 200 students from kindergarten to the 12th grade.

Visiting Matthew

At the small Christian school, everybody there knew Jesus, and most would speak as I moved from one class to the next. In the public school I attended, I missed the presence of the Holy Spirit, and I missed being accepted and recognized by my fellow students. So, after about two weeks, I was back at the Christian school and felt safe in the comfort of the Lord's provision for me.

As we walked back to our cabin, some of the saints we passed I had known on the earth. Each of them approached us and spoke of how wonderful it was when they had heard that I had joined them in Heaven. Wow, I felt so wonderful, loved, appreciated, and so connected to the family of God.

Then a man named Edward Eagle approached me, and he had such love for me in his eyes. He asked if I remembered him as we went to school together in the small Christian school I attended. I remembered him well. When I was fourteen years old, my parents were going through a divorce, and my world was turned upside down. I had anger within me that I really didn't know how to handle, and unfortunately, I turned it outward and became a bully to some of my fellow students. Edward was one of them, and I picked on him mercilessly, ridiculed him, fought him, and made it my purpose to humiliate him every chance I got.

Now, as I saw the love in his eyes towards me, I wept and begged him to forgive me for all that I had done to hurt him when we went to school together. He held nothing but love for me, and it was the pure love that could only come from Jesus. He told me that he had forgiven me and that it was all forgotten. We hugged, and I felt the love of Jesus flow into my heart from this man that I had been so hurtful to so many years ago.

Matthew looked on, and when we started walking again, he said to me, "Heaven is like that, dad. I've had the same thing happen to me, too." "Matthew, you have never hurt a soul in all of your life on the earth," I said to my son. "That's not exactly true, dad," Matthew said. "I did many selfish and hurtful things in my life on the earth, and I came to fully understand what I had done when I came here to Heaven."

We walked along talking, and I felt that incredible peace that passes all understanding that permeated all of Heaven and our hearts. It was so wonderful to be able to discuss things honestly without being bound to pride or some other type of defensiveness.

Matthew took me to a little park next to the river of life that flowed through all of Heaven. There we sat on a grassy knoll overlooking the river. There were many fruit trees everywhere in Heaven, and we ate some of the fruit. I chose a banana-looking fruit and a peach. Once again, I felt invigorated as I ate the fruit, and it filled me with such a feeling of completeness. They were extraordinary and unlike anything on earth. I felt so free in my every being.

Saints sat around the park on the grass and visited each other. I was reminded of pictures I had seen of the Victorian era with such a soft hue to them, capturing the peace and joy of the people of that era enjoying a day near the lake. Here, in Heaven, we all wore the white robes of righteousness, and there was no difference in each of us. One was not considered wealthy, and another was common or poor. All of us were blessed to be here with Jesus!

CHAPTER NINETEEN
A VISITOR AWAITS ME AT THE CABIN

After a period of time, we rose and started our journey back to the cabin. We approached the gates to the city that were always open and left the streets of gold to a beautiful path in such majestic beauty that it took your breath away. Soon we were approaching the cabin, and as we walked up, I saw my mother and grandparents sitting on the front porch swing, smiling and talking. "How did you enjoy your trip to the city?" My mother asked. "It was wonderful and exciting and, in some ways, difficult," I replied. "You must have gone to the Great Portal of Heaven," my mother commented.

"How did you know that?" I inquired. "Because I too went there to see what was going on with you and your brother when I first came to Heaven," my mother answered. "And as much as I loved to see you, it was hard seeing the warfare that is over God's people on the earth," my mother continued to say.

"Mom, you were the glue that held us all together and on track," I commented. "After you went to the Lord, my brother and I drifted apart. I would never have guessed when you were alive that it could happen. I thought we would always be there for each other. But I found out that after you went to glory, we spoke less and less. I tried to keep up and would call on holidays and special occasions. But he seemed to have little interest in keeping up with me," I said.

"Your brother loves you, and he has always had a problem showing affection and keeping in touch with family," I responded. "After I lost everything about four years after you went to be with the Lord, he seemed to have a different impression of me. It hurt when I saw him looking at me like I was a loser," I said in reply. "Well, he was still there to help you, wasn't he?" My mother responded. "Yes. Praise God that he did, for, without that help, my life would have been exceedingly hard," I replied. "He told me that I didn't have to pay him back, and he meant it. But I felt called by the Lord to pay him back, and I did, but it took me ten years to do it," I replied. "After that, I believe that he had a greater respect for me because I had done the right thing in paying him back," I continued to explain.

My mother smiled and said, "It always pays to follow the Lord!" "How right you are, Mom!" I replied. "Well, come on inside. We have a visitor that I know you will enjoy meeting," my mother said. "Who is that?" I inquired.

"I don't want to ruin the surprise." My mother said and opened the door to the cabin and walked inside in front of us. I waited respectfully as my grandparents went ahead of Matthew and me. When I entered the cabin, there, sitting on my couch in front of the fire, was John Denver.

CHAPTER TWENTY
JOHN DENVER IN HEAVEN

John Denver! I exclaimed. "Oh, how much I have wanted to meet you and speak to you," I said, walking towards him as he stood to meet me. He looked like I had remembered him when I was in my late teens, and he was in his thirties. He had joy that exuded all over his countenance. How much I had admired this man when he was on the earth. I was drawn to his music that lifted the beauty of the mountains, the love of simple things, and truth often found in the country but seldom in the city.

I had been so drawn to him that I imagined moving to Aspen, Colorado, and finding a way of life out there simply to be close to him and what he held dear. Later, as I matured, I realized the inability to satisfy my inner desires by drawing to the earth. I recalled a time when my mother had a convention that she attended in one of the summer months, and it was in Aspen, Colorado. I had driven from my home in Miami, Florida, to be with her, and we had a room at one of the ski resorts in Snowmass, a ski resort in Aspen.

I still had that desire to experience the freedom of the mountains, and as I began to look for a place to hike up a mountain around the resort, all I saw were "No Trespassing" signs. I found the same just about every place I went looking for a place to hike. That was an eye-opener for me. Instead of the freedom of the mountains, I saw commercialism everywhere I looked and private property. After that, I was no longer so naïve about the music of John Denver or the vision of the freedom he lifted up. I did continue to highly admire him and still longed to have the opportunity to meet him.

I had once seen him in a concert in Tallahassee, Florida. I was astounded that he came out on the stage first by himself as they introduced him simply as Mr. John Denver. He stood alone on the stage and played his guitar for a song or two and then began inviting the rest of his band one by one to join him. I thought at the time, what courage to stand there by himself without a band to help cover any mistakes. I was most impressed by how much love I felt from him as he spoke to the people and how he seemed genuinely concerned about their well-being by expressing to the crowd to be careful and have a safe drive home. Now I was meeting John Denver in Heaven!

"John, I heard that you had come home to be with us, and I wanted to welcome you home, brother, and give you a hug!" Denver said to me as he leaned over and gave me a brotherly hug. "John," I said as I reached over to him to hug him back, "I was so concerned that you did not know the Lord. I am so grateful to see you here in Heaven." I had tears of joyfulness knowing that John Denver had made it to Heaven.

John motioned to the couch in front of the fireplace, so I followed him around the sofa and sat next to him. He leaned forward and looked at me. "John, you were right to be concerned," Denver said and then went on to say, "I wasted the entire gift that God had given to me. I could have used my notoriety, music, following, and wealth to spread the gospel worldwide, and countless souls could have been saved if I had only yielded to the Lord. Instead, I was so caught up in myself that I forgot the Lord and all He had blessed me with. He had given me gifts and a life beyond what most people could ever imagine."

Visiting Matthew

"How did you know about me, John?" I asked. "Jesus asked me to come by and see you," John replied. "There are many people that loved me on the earth and would have sincerely led me in the right direction. You were one of them, John. I was meant to meet you, and we would have been friends. Instead, I surrounded myself with people that told me what I wanted to hear, and they used me and my success and then abandoned me when my success began to slip away," Denver said.

"When did you invite Jesus into your heart?" I asked John Denver. "I was just a little boy of seven years old," Denver responded.

"What happened?" I asked. "How did you get so far away from Jesus?" I asked. "When I first got into the music scene," John said, "I started using marijuana, and it opened my mind to the enemy."

"As I grew in success, I left Jesus behind. I never completely rejected Him. I just began to think that there were many ways to Heaven. I began to believe that God simply weighed the heart of men and that Jesus was not the only way into Heaven. I loved all men but in the wrong way as I did not love them in truth.

I also got caught up in American Indian mythology and believed that the earth was my mother. I exalted the earth in my music and loved and worshiped the creation rather than the creator of Heaven and earth. Because of my folly, I led countless people away from the truth. It is only in God's mercy and grace that I even got into Heaven."

"I am so sorry, John," I replied. "No. I am the one that is sorry, John," Denver said. "I also led you astray with my music, and I ask you to forgive me," Denver appealed to me with tears in his eyes. "Of course, I forgive you, John," I responded. "I love you, and I am so happy to see you in

Heavenly realms. I praise God that you are here. You cannot imagine how I anguished after you were killed in that airplane accident that you had missed Heaven and had gone to that horrible place of death and separation from God called Hell."

Denver was a pilot and a mighty fine pilot at that. At the time of his death, he had just purchased a home-built sports plane that he would use just for fun flying and not for travel. It had a rear engine and was capable of high speeds and sharp turns. It was a one-seater and only held the pilot with no room for passengers.

On the day he died, he took the plane up for a few "touch and goes," which are approaches to an airport runway, a touch down, and then acceleration back into flight. He was flying into a small airport near the Pacific Ocean and had gone out over the ocean, turned, and headed back to the airport when something terrible happened.

The National Transportation Safety Board determined that he had run out of fuel in his primary tank and struggled to switch to the reserve tank when he went down. Witnesses saw the plane dive straight into the Pacific from about five hundred feet above the water. I had always felt that the outcome of the investigation was wrong. Partly because I knew what a truly outstanding pilot Denver was and partly because it did not ring true to my spirit.

I had a sense that one of the cables broke that controlled the elevator and that when it broke, it forced the plane violently down. The aircraft was utterly destroyed in the accident, and it was difficult to determine the exact cause of the crash.

"John, may I ask you what happened in the accident? Why did your plane crash into the Pacific Ocean?" I asked. "John, I knew where the knob was to shift the fuel tanks, and that plane would have still flown even without fuel and the engine dead. It would have glided at the speed I was going, which was almost one hundred and eighty knots. What happened was that a cable snapped, and it forced me into the Pacific Ocean at over one hundred and eighty knots." Denver replied.

"When I went into the water, I thought I was perfectly fine as I rose from the plane and headed for the surface, and then the angels helped me, and we rose to Heaven." "It was just that fast, and I was never so glad to see Jesus." John Denver continued. "I ran to His loving arms, and He held me, and I wept and wept at my folly."

We stood up at that point and hugged, and I felt the love of Jesus flow between us. Then Matthew came over, and we had a group hug. Matthew had tears in his eyes as he told Denver how much he loved him. It was a glorious reunion between us all, and my heart felt full and overflowing with the Love of Jesus and for John Denver and Matthew. I walked out on the porch with Denver, and he turned and waved as he walked up the path. I knew that we would see each other many times again as we lived in this Heavenly Paradise for Eternity.

CHAPTER TWENTY-ONE
MY SECOND PRAYER IN HEAVEN: SKIING WITH MATTHEW

Matthew, I said, "I feel like I need to rest. I have seen so much today about the rebellion of Lucifer in Heaven, and I need to process it with Jesus." "I understand, dad," Matthew responded. "Go get some rest, and I love you."

I went up the stairs and looked over the banister to the living room below, with the beautiful fire burning in the fireplace. Matthew was sitting before the fire with his hands raised, praising God for His goodness and grace. It washed me through and through with thankfulness for the goodness God had given in this beautiful home called Heaven.

Matthew started singing a beautiful song of praise, and as he sang, I raised my arms and began singing along with him this beautiful song of praise. Oh, what a wonderful presence of God's Holy Spirit washed over and through me. "Matthew," I called from upstairs, "I love you!" "I love you too, dad," Matthew said as he looked up to me with a big smile of peace on his face. I turned and entered my room, knelt at the bedside, and prayed.

I felt such a beautiful presence of the Lord around me, and His presence felt so wonderful, so peaceful, so complete, and right in every way. "Father, I come before you in Jesus' Name and thank you for this day, my first day in Heaven. How wonderful Heaven is, and being in Your presence is always so glorious. Thank you for Your great love, Father. Thank You for all that you did for me today and all that You revealed to me today about the rebellion of Lucifer. I am so thankful that You are who You are, Father, and that You have such a great love for us. Thank You for preparing a place for me and for being together with my family. I know that I need to go to see the Fall of Adam and complete the story of what I began to see today. Strengthen me and give me the wisdom to see and understand all that You have called me to receive and show me the exact time that I should go to complete the experience.

I pray for my beloved wife and daughter, and I pray that You will continue to strengthen them to do all that must be done, and may they have their eyes upon You. Please send mighty angels to cover and protect them. I pray all of this in the glorious name of your beloved Son, Jesus. Amen.

Then I again heard my Father's voice audibly with strength, force, and tempered with love, "My son, have peace, for I have sent my angels to be with your family as they proceed through this time. All is well, my son. All is well! Rest in my love, and you will soon return to experience the fall of man. Again, I say rest in my love."

I got up from my knees, lay on the bed, and closed my eyes. I saw a ski lodge before me. It looked like the Sugar Mountain Ski Lodge that I had taken Matthew and his sister to in North Carolina when they were children. It was snowing, great flakes of snow, and Matthew was as he is now in Heaven, in his twenties, and he was standing beside me.

We were both dressed in the attire of skiers with bib overalls and down-filled heavy jackets. We were both using our poles to head to the nearest ski lift. Around us were countless other people dressed as we were in warm ski-type clothing. There was a thick blanket of fresh white snow on the ground, and it continued to fall in big clumps. It was cold, but with our warm clothing on, we were warm and toasty.

Dean Morphonios

I felt joy at being with Matthew in such a beautiful place, spending time together on the slopes. Matthew had joy on his face, too, and smiled back at me. We both got into position and felt the lift gently catch us up, and then we were riding up the slope of the mountain. Trees--oak, pine, maple, beech, and birch--bordered the slopes, and they were draped with the newly fallen snow.

I looked at Matthew and asked, "Where are we, Matthew?" "We are in Heaven, dad," Matthew responded. "How can that be?" I asked. I had just laid down on my bed to rest. "Jesus is giving us this time together like we were on the earth," Matthew responded. "You mean to say that this is not a dream?" I asked. "Well, it kind of is, and it is not," Matthew responded.

We reached the top of the lift and skied off the lift. We both looked down the slope. It was a gentle one. We lowered our goggles and, with poles in hand, headed together down the slope. It was exhilarating! We felt the brisk cold air rushing past us as we skied right and left, with the snow spraying up as our skis edged into it. Over moguls, Matthew headed off to my right and then joined me again as we skied down the slope to the bottom. We both looked at each other and smiled.

CHAPTER TWENTY-TWO
JESUS TEACHES ABOUT THE BATTLE FOR THE SOULS OF MEN

I opened my eyes. Jesus was sitting in the chair in my room watching me. "Did you rest well?" Jesus asked. "Master," I exclaimed as I rose from the bed and fell at His feet. I worshiped at Jesus' feet, completely broken before Him. I could only weep at His feet. I saw the holes that once a Roman nail passed through, and I felt so much love for my Savior. I was lost in my worship. I felt the Hand of Jesus upon my head, and he spoke, "Rise John and let us visit for a while." I rose from my knees, and Jesus beckoned me once again to sit beside him.

"Master," I asked, "May I inquire what just happened as I closed my eyes to rest?" "John, I know you better than anybody on earth, and I know what you need and when you need it," Jesus responded. "I just gave you and Matthew some time together on the slopes of Sugar Mountain, North Carolina." I was stunned at the answer and yet thrilled at the thought of it. Heaven continued to have surprises at every turn. "Master, I cannot tell you how exhilarating it was to be there with Matthew. I so wish that my daughter and wife could have been there with us." I spoke. "I know, John," Jesus said. "But you must remember that my daughters will be with us soon. You have an eternity to be together," Jesus said.

"Master, may I ask how long is soon?" I asked. "John," Jesus said, "Time is relative to where you are. Time on the earth seems to be so long, and yet time in Heaven is so short." I thought about what Jesus said for a moment and said, "so we are moving in a different time period here in

Heaven?" Jesus smiled and just said, "Have Peace, John. We will all be together soon, and very soon."

"Master," I asked, "May I ask you something?" "Of course, John," Jesus said. "I am wondering about the mind-binding attacks I saw in the war in Heaven. I expected more of the physical attacks we see in warfare on the earth," I spoke.

"John," Jesus said, "Angels are spirit beings. They are bodiless beings. Man is made up of a physical body, a spirit, and a soul. During warfare on the earth, where men fight men, the purpose is to injure or kill another man. So, to kill the enemy is to kill the physical body of the enemy. Remember, my Father made man in His own image. So, mankind has eternal life because he was a spirit either here in Heaven or hell with Satan and his fallen angels. It is the spirit of a man that is born again when one accepts Me as their Lord and Savior. A man's soul is the man's mind, will, and emotions, Jesus said.

"So, you are saying that angels do not have a body to kill as a man has?" I asked. "That's right, John." Jesus went on to say, "and if you consider what transpires in spiritual warfare on the earth, fallen angels (what men call demons and what I will refer to as the kingdom of darkness that represents Satan and his fallen angels), fight to destroy men. They base their warfare on hatred of My Father and Me and our kingdom of light and glory on earth and in Heaven.

On a foundational level, the kingdom of darkness makes every effort to keep from My Father and Me every man, woman, and child they can deceive, steal, kill and destroy. Their goal is to blind and deafen every man, woman, and child so they never accept me as their personal savior and thereby have their spirits born again in Me. Every person that does not come to Me is not born again and dies in their sin.

Hell was created for Satan and his fallen angels. Mankind was never meant to go there. Satan knows that every man, woman, and child that he deceives into not accepting Me as their Lord and Savior will essentially be separated from my Father and Me and spend eternity in torment in that horrible place. My Father and I love all men, women, and children. We don't want any of my Father's children to know that horrible place."

"Any man that accepts me as Lord and Savior, their spirit is instantly born again, and the kingdom of darkness loses that spirit. However, Satan and his fallen angels don't give up at that point and quit fighting over that person. Their emphasis shifts to a fight over that person's call and destiny so that the kingdom of darkness will now attempt to keep that person from being a light in the darkness and from leading others to make a choice for me. All of my Father's children should be fulfilling the great commission by telling others about God's goodness and His great love for mankind. They should be telling others that He gave the life of His only begotten Son for their eternal salvation. This salvation is for all that accept the gift."

"Many in your time on the earth, John, accepted my gift of salvation but made no effort to share me with a lost and dying world. Many were so caught up in their own lives and their desire to be accepted by the world that they denied Me and hid Me and were ashamed of Me. They cared more about the acceptance of men than the acceptance of God their Father."

"This is a great sorrow to most men, especially when they leave their lives and go on to live for eternity in Heaven. The kingdoms of darkness are masters of deceiving men of their eternal salvation and stopping them from their witness, call, destiny, and rewards in Heaven. They do this by tempting men using the temptations of the flesh, and they use thoughts and feelings to lure men into sinning against my Father and me."

"What you saw in the warfare in Heaven was the warfare between angels fighting with mind-binding warfare between bodiless spirits," Jesus went on to describe. "Satan uses the same warfare on the earth to attack men and draw them away from me, often using the temporal pleasures of the flesh. John, remember in my Word, my servant Paul wrote by inspiration of My Spirit in Galatians 5.

Galatians 5:16-25 (KJV) This I say then, Walk in the Spirit, and ye shall not fulfil the lust of the flesh. 17 For the flesh lusteth against the Spirit, and the Spirit against the flesh: and these are contrary the one to the other: so that ye cannot do the things that ye would. 18 But if ye be led of the Spirit, ye are not under the law. 19 Now the works of the flesh are manifest, which are these; Adultery, fornication, uncleanness, lasciviousness, 20 Idolatry, witchcraft, hatred, variance, emulations, wrath, strife, seditions, heresies, 21 Envyings, murders, drunkenness, revellings, and such like: of the which I tell you before, as I have also told you in time past, that they which do such things shall not inherit the kingdom of God. 22 But the fruit of the Spirit is love, joy, peace, longsuffering, gentleness, goodness, faith, 23 Meekness, temperance: against such there is no law. 24 And they that are Christ's have crucified the flesh with the affections and lusts. 25 If we live in the Spirit, let us also walk in the Spirit.

The kingdom of darkness uses their mind attacks on men to draw them into "adultery, fornication, uncleanness, lasciviousness, idolatry, witchcraft, hatred, variance, emulations, wrath, strife, seditions, heresies, envying, murders, drunkenness and reveling." (Galatians 5:19-21 KJV). Once they have snared them in the place of death, their eyes are blinded to the truth. Some get free, but most die in their sin and never come to know me. Each of these sins of the flesh has temporal pleasures for those engaged in the folly of such corruption. But the end is death.

"When the kingdom of darkness attacks a man," Jesus said, "they use suggestions in their mind. Those in the kingdom of darkness reason with men why they should be able to go forward with the sin they are being tempted by. Then, they will repeatedly pepper their prey with the suggestion of the sin, repeating it and giving a feeling of lust for the sin until they have snared their prey. The poor soul that does not know My ways or My Word and has not submitted to My Father and Me does nothing to resist Satan and his fallen angels. They are then led like cattle to the slaughter. By the time they figure out that it is a trap, it is often too late. The sin opens the door for Satan and his fallen angels to put sickness, disease, and infirmity on their prey. Their goal is to ensnare a soul, bring them to death, and ultimately drag their soul into hell."

"While on earth, did you ever see a flying insect caught in a spider's web?" Jesus asked. "Yes," I responded. "Well, it is much that way with Satan and his webs. Once the prey is trapped, he begins to spin the web around his prey, which blinds and deafens them to the truth. They are so entangled that they are dead before they feel the effects of the death upon their body."

"In the war in Heaven," Jesus said, "you saw angels drawing other angels into the conspiracy to revolt and rebel against My Father and His Kingdom of Light. They too were reasoning with them in their hatred, and the darkness was divided from the light."

"Is this the same warfare that happens to one facing sickness, disease, and infirmity to keep them from receiving their healing?" I asked? "Among my children, a great body of believers now understand that I was wounded for their transgressions, bruised for their iniquities, the chastisement of their peace was upon me, and by my stripes, they are healed. My servant Isaiah prophesied it in the 53rd chapter of Isaiah," Jesus said. "However, the warfare over one believing for healing is often great as the enemy squeezes them so that they will not receive the truth. It is the truth that sets my people free.

Satan will hit them with mind-binding attacks from the enemy who whispers in their ear and causes them to reject the one I have sent to pray for their healing. They will begin to see the intercessor as a "fanatic." They will start to believe and imagine they will never be healed because they cannot actually see it in the spiritual realm. Although some I give in my mercy, most healings must be obtained by faith."

"Satan and his fallen angels use fear to have my children struck with illness, proclaim and confess their illness multiple times to multiple people. Then when Satan and their fallen angels have sealed their fate with their own words, they will hit these same children with hopelessness. Without hope, there is no life. There are also entire religions that reject my healing miracles because they cannot accept that I still perform miracles," Jesus said. "They have no faith for a miracle and readily accept what the enemy whispers in their ear as the fact that healing is within my omnipotence, and it is the mysterious will of God that some receive healing, and others don't. In so doing, they then reject me and the gospel of my healing virtue even though they have

Visiting Matthew

My Word and know that I healed all that even touched the hem of my robe.

Gospel means Good News, and an essential part of my Gospel is the Good News of my healing virtue that is always my Father's will," Jesus said. As long as Christians believe that the one who receives healing is a choice based upon God's arbitrary will, those Christians have no responsibility to believe and receive. There is no faith in such of my children for healing, and they often do not receive their healing, and that further solidifies their mistaken doctrine. Some of my children even go so far as to proclaim that "gifts of healing" no longer exist for the modern church and that such gifts died with the last apostle. This doctrine is a lie perpetrated by Satan to mislead my children and deny them the miracles that I bring to a believer's life.

CHAPTER TWENTY-THREE
WALKING WITH MATTHEW TO HEAVENLY JERUSALEM

I then thanked the Master for explaining how the battle is fought both in Heaven and earth. Jesus then looked me in the eyes and began to speak about the fall of man.

"John," Jesus said, "I came to talk to you about your visit to see the fall of man. I want you to go back now and finish the encounter with the actual fall of man." "Yes, Master," I said. "There is a reason why I need you to experience that encounter as I am going to bring you higher, for you need to know certain things before you can go higher." "Yes, Lord," I replied. "I feel rested and ready now to experience the fall of man. How shall I go to the city?" I asked. "I have asked Matthew to take you back to the city," Jesus said. "Yes, Master," I replied. Jesus then stood, and we walked out together down the stairs.

Matthew was sitting in the living room before the fire, still praising the Lord. As we walked into the living room, Matthew fell to his knees and began worshiping Jesus. I too quickly fell to my knees also, and we worshiped at the feet of our Glorious Lord! As we worshiped Him, it seemed like a chorus of angels also began to praise Him. I had never felt such love for Jesus. Oh, how much I loved Him and adored Him. I wanted to stay there at his feet forever!

Soon, Jesus laid His hands upon us both, and we rose and went to His loving arms and held Him together. What glory! His Love enveloped us, and I can honestly say that I had never felt such love at any time in my life on earth. It was the same Love that permeated Heaven. What a glorious

Visiting Matthew

love! Then we walked out together with our hearts burning within us as we walked like the two that were on the road to Emmaus. We walked outside the cabin together and up the path back towards the city. As we reached the main path back up to the city, Jesus beckoned us farewell and took a way to the left. Matthew and I continued towards the city, watching as others on the path came to Jesus to hug and love Him.

We walked along quietly, pondering all that had just transpired with Jesus. Matthew spoke up first, "Well, dad, what do you think of Heaven?" Matthew asked. "Matthew," I replied, "It is everything that I ever thought it would be and more. I have never felt so wonderful and at home. I feel the love of God everywhere I have been, and every moment is Heavenly! Being with Jesus and my family and knowing that we will never be apart again is joy unspeakable and full of God's glory!" I responded. "I feel the same way, dad, and I can't wait for my sister to join us. How wonderful it will be for us all to be together," Matthew responded.

As we walked toward God's Holy Mountain, I could see the City of Jerusalem up on the mountain shining like a jewel. "Matthew," I asked, "Why don't we live in the City of Jerusalem?" "Dad," Matthew replied, "We didn't serve God with our whole hearts." "I understand," I said, knowing the truth about what Matthew had just told me.

It could not be denied. All of us, Matthew, my mother and grandparents, and me too, lived our lives in compromise instead of serving God with all that we had to give. We loved God and Jesus, but we also loved the things of the world. Jesus said:

Matthew 19:29 (KJV) And every one that hath forsaken houses, or brethren, or sisters, or father, or mother, or wife, or children, or lands, for my name's sake, shall receive an hundredfold, and shall inherit everlasting life.

I had to honestly say that I was one of those that did not forsake all for Jesus. I held onto my life and holding on kept me from following after Jesus with every part of my being and forsaking all for Him.

I found that I was not disturbed by the truth of that fact. God is perfect and just in all that He does. He is the perfect judge of all men, and He knew the truth about my life and the choices that I had made. I could have justified them with reasons such as I had to provide for my family or I could not go anywhere for Jesus because I had a family to look after. I had to be responsible with our money as I had to set it aside for the future.

There was no question about what I could have done for Jesus if I had forsaken all. The truth was that I knew the truth and simply refused to renounce all for Jesus. Now, I did abandon some things for Him. I set myself apart from the world, and I supported His work in ministries that I used the tithe to help support. However, what I didn't do was the "all" part. That was where I compromised and held back, and I was genuinely sorry.

Matthew spoke again, bringing me back to our walking down the path towards the City of Jerusalem. "Dad," Matthew said, "I know how it made me feel to realize that I could have done so much more for Jesus if I had only forsaken all for Him. But the important thing is that we did choose Jesus, and we live for eternity with Him in heavenly realms."

Matthew continued to encourage me with words of truth about our life in Heaven. I was really taking in all of the truth about my life and my eternity with a remarkable thankfulness for being in Heaven. I realized that, like so many that lived on earth, I could have missed Heaven and ended up in Hell. I was fortunate enough to have others who witnessed to me and led me to where I accepted Jesus as my Lord and Savior. More importantly, I would live forever in this beautiful place, and I had the blessings of my family with me, and we were all living in Heaven with Jesus. It was Heavenly!

"Matthew," I said, "I love you, and I am so sorry that I did not forsake all for Jesus, but I thank God for His mercy and grace and that I have the grace of living here with you and my family in Heaven. Will there ever be a time that I will go before the throne of God and answer for my life on earth?" I asked. "Dad," Matthew said, "I went before the throne shortly after coming to Heaven. I am not sure why you have not been before the throne yet. Everything God does is great and wonderful, so there has to be a reason that you do not know yet." "Well," I said, "I am just going to give it to Jesus and trust Him."

CHAPTER TWENTY-FOUR
BACK TO THE TIME PORTAL

We had come to the place where we were walking up to the Gates of Jerusalem. They were magnificent, and I could not help but remember John's description of them from the Book of Revelation, chapter 21.

Revelation 21:21 (KJV) And the twelve gates were twelve pearls; every several gate was of one pearl: and the street of the city was pure gold, as it were transparent glass.

The Gates were massive and reached the top of the wall that went around the city, constructed of jewels and precious stones. The saints were going in and out, and we joined the saints, moving now through the gates and into the City of Jerusalem.

We walked on streets of pure gold, and it was so pure that it was translucent. We passed buildings and homes. Fruit trees lined the streets. Multiple streets came off the main street where we walked, and each was named after a famous saint in the Bible. Up ahead, the street was divided, with half going to the right and half going to the left around the large crystal-type building that was set apart.

"Matthew," I asked, "What is this building called where we are translated into various places in the history of God's People?" "It's called the "Time Portal," Matthew responded. "Time Portal," I asked, "You're kidding me, right?" "No, dad," Matthew responded, "That is what it is really called. Think about it, it is a time portal, and you get to go back to any time in the history of God's Kingdom and see firsthand what happened. Pretty neat building, isn't it?" "You bet, Matthew!" I responded.

We entered the building again through the revolving door. Matthew and I entered together and pushed the door to the place where we stepped into the building. I saw angels helping the saints and directing them to certain pedestals within the building, and I was looking for Andrew. I saw him at about the same time he spotted us.

"Hi, John, Hi Matthew," Andrew said, "Are you ready for the rest of your journey into "The Fall of Man?" "Yes, Andrew," I responded and said, "You remembered." "I did," Andrew responded. Also, "Jesus came by and told me that you were coming."

I hugged Matthew, and he said that he would be here waiting when I returned to walk back home. Andrew led me back to the pedestal in which I had been transported to witness the rebellion of Lucifer. Since I knew what to do, I put out my hand and touched the pedestal and was immediately transported to earth.

CHAPTER TWENTY-FIVE
THE GARDEN OF EDEN AND ADAM

I stood looking at a beautiful land that had a river flowing through it. It had the appearance of Heaven, but I knew that it was the earth. The grasses, the trees, and the vegetation all were perfect in every respect. Flowers and fruit trees were everywhere but especially along the riverbank. There were large, beautiful areas of soft heaven grass. I was barefoot, and I enjoyed how the grass felt on my bare feet. I could feel the presence of God coming up through my bare feet through the grass.

I knew instinctively that this was the Garden of Eden. It was perfect in every way. It was lush and full of life. Like Heaven, it had nothing that would hurt or harm but was a true oasis. I wandered around looking at the garden, and I specifically went to look for the center of the garden, where I knew from God's Word that I would find the two trees in the midst of the garden: the Tree of Life and the Tree of Knowledge of Good and Evil.

I saw them up ahead, and I found that both trees were pleasant to look upon, but which tree was which? I reasoned that the Tree of Life would not be as inviting as the Tree of Knowledge of Good and Evil. The tree I thought was the Tree of Life had fruit hanging from its branches that looked like pomegranates. But the tree itself had small rugged-looking leaves, and it was not very inviting.

The tree I thought was the tree of Knowledge of Good and Evil appeared to have fruit that looked like peaches. I thought how ironic it was that I was looking upon a "peach tree" and not the "apple tree" that man so often depicted as the tree of Knowledge of Good and Evil. I couldn't help but laugh at how the State of Georgia had made the "Peach" a symbol for their state. Oh well. How could they have known?

Of course, I later found out that I was right in my analysis, and each tree was as I suspected. What was that old cliché from the earth, "Don't judge a book by its cover!

As I continued to watch, I saw God the Father walking through the Garden of Eden in a white robe. I knew that He was the Father, as He glowed with the Glory of God that beamed from Him like the sun. I saw God begin to form man from the dust of the earth. He gathered handfuls of dirt and began to form man in the midst of the air with His hands molding and shaping, and I began to see the figure of a man emerge from the form. When He was done, the man looked grey and was lifeless with his head slumped forward. There was no life in him. He was entirely without life.

I saw God lay the man down on the ground on his back. I saw God stretch over the man with God's palms on man's palms, God's eyes looking into the lifeless eyes of man, God's body lying on top of the man exact feet to feet, knees to knees, hip to hip, chest to chest and face to face and God breathed into man's nostrils.

Genesis 2:7 (KJV) And the LORD God formed man of the dust of the ground, and breathed into his nostrils the breath of life; and man became a living soul.

God's life entered into man, and man became alive, and man shined with the glory of God. The man God called Adam looked just like God the Father, although he was naked, and God the Father had a robe on. The man did not appear naked because of his innocence and because he was clothed in the glory of God, much like a little child does not appear naked even though they might have no clothes on.

God began to walk with the man around the Garden of Eden, and he showed him the trees and the river, and I saw him instruct the man about the Tree of Knowledge of Good and Evil. God was emphatic with the man Adam explaining to him that he was not to eat of it and that on the day that he would eat of the fruit of the tree, he would surely die. I could see that Adam received and understood that he was not to eat of the Tree of Knowledge of Good and Evil.

Genesis 2:16-17 (KJV) And the LORD God commanded the man, saying, Of every tree of the garden thou mayest freely eat: 17 But of the tree of the knowledge of good and evil, thou shalt not eat of it: for in the day that thou eatest thereof thou shalt surely die.

God the Father and Adam spoke easily with each other about the Garden, and God brought all of the animals, insects, and every other created being to Adam and watched as Adam named each one. I had never heard the language that God the Father and Adam spoke, but somehow, I understood what they were saying to each other. I could tell that Adam had a superior intellect, and it flowed easily as he studied each creature that God the Father brought before him, and he readily named each one. "Ant, Spider, Bird, Cow, Dog, Fox, Skunk, Lion, Bobcat, Cat, Giraffe, Rhinoceros, Tiger, Bear, Alligator, Monkey" and on and on it went as Adam readily named each.

As each creature was named, I heard the creature speak to Adam with words of thankfulness and respect. I was taken aback by this fact. They all spoke! Then I remembered that the serpent also talked to Adam and his wife and realized that before the fall, it was not considered unusual for the creatures of the garden to speak with Adam and his wife.

All animals, insects, and every other created being were harmless to Adam. They were all passive, and there was no fear between the man Adam and the creatures he named. God the Father watched on as a good father overseeing all that transpired. He had a very watchful eye over Adam, and it appeared to me that the Father measured if any comfort would come to Adam with his interaction with the creatures he named.

I could see that after a while, the man Adam would tire. He would gather some fruit from several of the many fruit trees that abounded in the garden, eat the fruit, and drink the water in the river. Then Adam would lie down in the soft heavenly grass under one of the trees and fall fast asleep. As night entered the Garden of Eden, a mist descended, and all the trees, grass, and plants were watered with what appeared like dew when I was on the earth.

During the night season, God the Father would go back to Heaven and then return the following day after the man Adam had rested. Then they would again walk and talk together and engage in the process of naming the creatures of the garden.

I could tell that the man Adam was lonely, and of course, God the Father could tell also. I knew this about our Heavenly Father. He knows our needs and wants to provide us with the desires of our hearts. It is not always possible because we do not trust Him. But that is a lack of faith on our part, not on His.

CHAPTER TWENTY-SIX
THE GARDEN OF EDEN AND ADAM AND ADAM

Then I watched as God put a deep sleep over the man Adam and as he lay in a deep sleep, God the Father reached down with His right hand and took a rib out of Adam's chest. He withdrew His hand with the rib, and the place where God the Father removed it immediately closed up as if his chest had never been opened. Then God the Father put the rib on the ground, and immediately He created the woman from the rib of Adam's own body.

Genesis 2:21-22 (KJV) And the LORD God caused a deep sleep to fall upon Adam, and he slept: and he took one of his ribs, and closed up the flesh instead thereof; 22 And the rib, which the LORD God had taken from man, made he a woman, and brought her unto the man.

Once He created the woman, she was like the man Adam before God the Father breathed life into him. She was grey and lifeless. God the Father lay her on the ground on her back, and He did the same as with Adam. He stretched over the woman with His palms on the woman's palms and His eyes looking into the lifeless eyes of the woman. God's body lying on top of the woman exact feet to feet, knees to knees, hip to hip, chest to chest, and face to face, and God breathed into the woman's nostrils. The woman now became a living soul, and she sat up and looked around. Like the man Adam, she was naked but clothed with the glory of God, and like Adam, she did not appear naked in her innocence.

God then awakened the man Adam, and as Adam awakened, he saw the woman sitting there, and he rose from the ground and stood next to God, watching the woman. God the Father spoke to Adam and explained to him that He had created the woman out of a rib from his own body, and then God the Father presented the woman to Adam.

I saw Adam help the woman up, and he held both of the woman's hands and looked into her eyes. Then he reached his arms around her and held her close, and the woman held Adam close. I saw God the Father smile.

Genesis 2:23 (KJV) And Adam said, This is now bone of my bones, and flesh of my flesh: she shall be called Woman, because she was taken out of Man.

When God created man and woman, He called them Adam.

Genesis 5:2 (KJV) Male and female created he them; and blessed them, and called their name Adam, in the day when they were created.

I thought that odd when I heard God call "them" Adam, and then I remembered that God always looks upon a husband and wife as having one flesh.

I thought of my own wife back on the earth and how much I loved her. When we were married, we had the minister read this very verse from Genesis 5:2 as it represented the covenant love we felt for each other. I also thought of why adultery is such a serious sin in the eyes of God as it divides the oneness between a married couple. People simply have no understanding of how Satan works to destroy marriages as he is really trying to destroy the oneness of a married couple. He uses the lust for another man or woman to draw the married man or woman into a place of evil, breaking the covenant marriage between a married man and woman.

God is a covenant God, and He is in covenant with all that accept Jesus as their Lord and Savior. Covenant is simply a promise that is sealed with blood. When God sent His only begotten Son Jesus to die on the cross for our sins, He sealed His promise of eternal life with the blood of Jesus. A covenant sealed with blood cannot be broken, although it can be rejected if there is an affirmative rejection of that promise.

This covenant promise is why I had such confidence in my salvation when I was born again. Upon accepting the gift of salvation, a born-again man or woman, accepts that Jesus died on the cross for their sins. That is a covenant promise from God, and that promise is sealed with the blood of His Son Jesus.

In Christ, a genuinely married couple, like my wife and me, had what is known as an Adam-Adam relationship. We were one in every way, and when God looked upon us, He saw one.

When I lived on the earth, many people in the world were legally married by law but were never married of heart. I thought about how they held back from a heartfelt commitment to their spouse. A good analogy is a man who lusts for a woman in his mind but has no love in his heart for her. Satan uses this lustful love, which is not loving, to destroy lives.

God's way is seen by example in how he described the building of the tabernacle to Moses. He first began with the Ark of the Covenant placed within the Holiest of Holies, the very center and core of the Tabernacle and the place where the Spirit of the Lord would abide.

Exodus 25:10 (KJV) And they shall make an ark of shittim wood: two cubits and a half shall be the length thereof, and a cubit and a half the breadth thereof, and a cubit and a half the height thereof.

Exodus 25:22 (KJV) And there I will meet with thee, and I will commune with thee from above the mercy seat, from between the two cherubims which are upon the ark of the testimony, of all things which I will give thee in commandment unto the children of Israel.

So, it is with a man and a woman as God binds their hearts together in married love. God is a covenant God. Therefore, God expects His people to be covenant people. As God keeps His covenant promises to us, He expects us to keep our covenant promises with each other.

So, as it was with my wife and me, in God's eyes, a married couple is first covenant-bound together in the heart. This heart covenant is why Satan will try to bring division between a married couple and destroy the heart covenant between them.

CHAPTER TWENTY-SEVEN

DRAWN TO THE TREE OF KNOWLEDGE OF GOOD AND EVIL

A dam and his wife were beautiful in their natural being. Both appeared to be in their early twenties, and each had long, beautiful hair. Adam's hair was brown, and his wife's hair was a lighter shade and had the appearance of what people called "dirty blonde" when I was on the earth. They were both highly developed in their physique. They did not appear to have any fat but were healthy, toned, and strong. They glowed with the Glory of God that shined about them.

I watched as Adam and his wife walked around the Garden of Eden, and I could tell that Adam was excited to show his wife all that he knew about their new home. Adam was very intelligent, and he spoke of all the wonders that God the Father had revealed to him. He showed Eve the river Euphrates that ran through the midst of the garden and then showed her the beautiful flowers, shrubs, and trees.

As they walked through the garden, many of the wildlife came to them to be introduced to Adam's wife. Adam would speak to his wife about each one, and the animals spoke back to them. Adam's wife stroked the mane of the lion. I saw her scratch behind the ear of the bear. Adam picked up a mink and rubbed his face against the mink's belly, and the mink laughed. It was strange and yet comforting to watch their interaction with the wildlife. I thought to myself, "Well, they're never alone in the garden, that's for sure."

I watched as they stood before the Tree of Life and the Tree of Good and Evil. I could see Adam moving his head back and forth as he spoke to his wife that they were never to eat or even touch the Tree of Knowledge of Good and Evil.

I could see Adam and his wife standing there and looking intently at the Tree of Knowledge of Good and Evil, wondering about it. They looked back and forth between themselves and spoke. I could not hear exactly what they were saying but could pick up a word here and there. "It really doesn't look like it would harm anyone," Adam's wife was saying to him. "I know," Adam responded, "God said not to eat of it or even touch it for the day we do; we will die."

I saw that the tree was beginning to draw them, and they would stand there just looking and wondering. I was somewhat surprised that Adam and Eve were so drawn to the Tree of Knowledge of Good and Evil. They spent no time looking upon the Tree of Life, which did not appear very inviting. However, the Tree of Knowledge of Good and Evil was very inviting. It wasn't long before I saw the serpent come by and speak with Adam and his wife.

The Bible said Satan used the serpent for deception. From reading God's Word, I knew that the serpent was really Satan, who was a bodiless fallen angelic spirit. He, therefore, hijacked the serpent to use as a covering for his deception.

Genesis 3:1 (KJV) Now the serpent was more subtil than any beast of the field which the LORD God had made. And he said unto the woman, Yea, hath God said, Ye shall not eat of every tree of the garden?

Subtle is defined by the dictionary "as making use of clever and indirect methods to achieve something." What Satan was seeking to achieve here was a total coup over what God had done in giving authority over the Garden of Eden and, by interpretation, the earth to Adam and his wife.

In essence, Satan was setting a trap for God. He knew that God was made of love. As the fallen angel, he did not have the capability to love like God did because he was created to serve and could see no advantage in such feelings and emotions as love.

When he rebelled against God, he was filled with nothing but contempt for God, His Son Jesus, and the Holy Spirit. He believed that love would be God's weakness. Because God loved this creation, God called "man," Satan knew that if he could get this man to take the fruit of the Tree of Knowledge of Good and Evil, God would be bound to His Word. Therefore, Satan would then be able to kill Adam and take dominion of the Garden of Eden and, by extension, the earth. Then he would be in a position to hurt the heart of God. In that hurt, Lucifer surmised, he would then be able to ascend to the throne and take God's throne.

The serpent did not look like I had always seen snakes on the earth. It walked on four legs and could stand up on its hind legs the way a raccoon could stand. The serpent walked up to Adam and Eve as they looked upon the Tree of Knowledge of Good and Evil. "It sure looks like it would be good for eating," The serpent said. "Why don't you have some?" The serpent asked. Adam and his wife looked over at the serpent as he looked at the tree. "We may eat of the fruit of the trees of the garden, but the fruit of the tree, which is in the midst of the garden, God has said, we shall not eat of it, neither shall we touch it, lest we die," Adam's wife spoke back to the serpent.

I could see that the serpent had a silly grin on its face as he said back to Adam's wife, "You shall not surely die, for God does know that in the day you eat thereof, then your eyes shall be opened, and you shall be as gods, knowing good from evil."

I knew that part of the problem for Adam and his wife was a failure to have known God's Word. God never said that they could not touch the tree or the fruit of the Tree of Knowledge of Good and Evil. In fact, they could have picked every bit of fruit from the tree and presented it to the Father as an offering of love. It was God's fruit, and they should have respected that which was His and not stolen from their Father. This misunderstanding of the Word led them to think that what the Father told them was false, for they did not die when they touched the fruit.

Adam looked at his wife, and she looked back at him. Adam had never considered being like God the Father. Had God purposely kept something from him? He had trusted God and never questioned His reason for not eating from the Tree of Knowledge of Good and Evil. Was this tree in the Garden the gateway to being like God? He didn't like having feelings of distrust like this, especially about God, his Father. Why would God have kept something that fantastic from him?

Genesis 3:6 (KJV) And when the woman saw that the tree was good for food, and that it was pleasant to the eyes, and a tree to be desired to make one wise, she took of the fruit thereof, and did eat, and gave also unto her husband with her; and he did eat.

Adam's wife looked at the fruit and reasoned three things. The tree was good for food, pleasant to the eyes, and desired to make one wise. Satan will always offer reasons why you need to do something that you know is wrong or your inner witness tells you is wrong. Adam's wife was only fooling herself by coming up with reasons to do what God had told them specifically not to do.

I felt like shaking Adam and his wife and telling them, "Don't do it! Trust your Father! We have a loving and kind Father who always seeks the best for us. Don't you know that about Him? Kick that stupid serpent out of the Garden and tell him that he will not speak against your Father that way!" But I could only look on in wonder and disgust as I saw what was happening.

I saw Adam's wife look over at him and then back at the tree and back to Adam as she reached out and touched one of the fruits on the tree, pulling her hand back quickly. She looked at her hand, and Adam examined her hand, and they looked at each other and smiled. Then she reached over and caressed one of the peaches hanging from the tree, feeling its fuzzy skin, and brought her hand back, and once again, Adam and his wife examined his wife's hand looked back at each other, and smiled.

"You see," the serpent said, "I told you that you will not surely die!" Adam's wife then reached over, put her hand on one of the peaches, and pulled it off the tree, bringing it back to them. She looked at Adam and then at the fruit. "Go ahead," The serpent chided with her, "Eat it." Adam's wife then took a bite of the peach and smiled as the juice was sweet and good. She handed the peach to Adam, and he too took a bite, and as they smiled at each other, something terrible happened as the glory of God that enshrouded them lifted.

CHAPTER TWENTY-EIGHT
FALLING FROM GLORY

Adam looked at his wife, and she back at him, looking at each other up and down, and both realized they were naked. As the serpent laughed at them with glee in his eyes, they suddenly experienced a feeling they had never felt before. They felt fear. Adam's face contorted in fear, as did his wife, and they both ran towards some bushes, looking for something to cover their nakedness. All the while, the serpent laughed and laughed at their anguish.

People fail to calculate that they get more than they bargained for when they choose to go with Satan. Yield to a demonic spirit of thievery and steal something off a shelf in a store, and you will get a spirit of thievery as you have moved in agreement with that spirit. Yield to a spirit of lust, and you will get a spirit of lust, and so on and so on.

When Adam and his wife yielded to Satan's temptation, they not only opened the door to rebellion and disobedience of God's command but also felt an onslaught of evil spirits that now rushed upon them. Gone was the Peace of God and the Heavenly Glory of God that surrounded them. Now, they felt the pure evil of fear. Fear over what they had done, fear of being caught by God the Father. Fear of what was to become of them. Echoing in their ears were the Father's Words.

Genesis 2:16-17 (KJV) And the LORD God commanded the man, saying, Of every tree of the garden thou mayest freely eat: 17 But of the tree of the knowledge of good and evil,

*thou shalt not eat of it: for in the day that thou eatest thereof
thou shalt surely die.*

Ironically the words of Satan, "you will not surely
die," also echoed in their ears.

What Adam and his wife did not understand was that
God's Word was true. They were not dead physically. That
would take some time to play out. But that day, they indeed
died spiritually in the sense that they were separated from
God their Father. Of course, they were not separated from
their new father, Satan, who represented the personification
of a living death.

I thought of what Jesus said in the Book of John.

John 14:15 (KJV) If ye love me, keep my commandments.

When you fall in love with Jesus, it is easy to keep His
Commandments and Word. Love and obedience go
together. So, when Adam and his wife failed to obey God,
they did not move in love. Tragically, by following Satan,
they gave the authority that God had given to them over the
Garden of Eden, and by extension the earth, to Satan, and
Satan became the god of this world. In the process, Satan
and all of his fallen angels rushed into the world and were
now in authority over the man. Mankind became
subservient to them, at least as to men that are not born
again in Christ Jesus.

Adam and his wife had lost their innocence, and
having now the knowledge of good and evil, they
considered all their possibilities, and none of their options
looked good. They had opened a door that could not be
shut. They had crossed over into another dimension. Their
child-like simple faith was gone.

Visiting Matthew

Compare a child of the Lord who searches out the knowledge for an ache or pain on the internet. Instead of going to Jesus with a healing need, they reach for the Tree of Knowledge of Good and Evil. As they read the possibilities, they all seem endless and fearful.

They consider the spectrum and ponder where they might be on that spectrum. People's minds think through to the worst-case scenario, and their imaginations give it a three-dimensional look. Then they begin speaking about what they have researched and found. They seek medical assistance with panic rising within them about what the doctor might say to them after examining and determining that what they thought was true has indeed been confirmed. More often than not, they get a good report from the doctor. At least in comparison to the "worst-case scenario that Satan whispered into their ear. Then they laugh at their anxiousness and feel good that it was not as bad as they thought. That is just how it is with fear and the Tree of Knowledge of Good and Evil.

Satan has no power to create. Therefore, to create the evil, disorder, and death that he wants to bring to mankind, he must use people to do it. Man was created in God's image, and we can create with our words, just as God does.

When Satan attempts to bring sickness, disease, and infirmity into a person's life, he will bring a fear upon a person of having what he wants to put upon them. Cancer, heart issues, and physical and mental breakdowns must be created and established. Therefore, it is vital for a child of the Lord Jesus Christ to only speak the words of life.

When fear arises over a physical symptom, it is time to be cautious about words spoken forth that confirm that fear and establish it. Speak only the Word of God. If it is a healing concern, speak out loud, "I am the healed of the Lord!" Never speak contrary to the Word of God!

CHAPTER TWENTY-NINE
PANIC, FEAR, AND DENIAL

Adam felt panic rising within him. What were they going to do now? God always came to walk with them in the cool of the day to spend time with them. How were they going to hide what they had done? Adam went back to the Tree of Knowledge of Good and Evil and found the remnants of the peach on the ground and hurriedly picked up every trace of it and threw it into one of the shrubs. He then rushed back to the bushes where he and his wife had hidden, and they found some large fig leaves. They were able to use a thin root to bind them together front and back for both him and his wife. Although awkward, he was at least successful in covering their nakedness.

I thought how silly it seemed to see Adam and his wife trying so hard to hide what was impossible to hide. But in truth, that is the way it is with sin. Sin always causes a separation between God and his children. Sin will always cause a child of God to hide after sinning. Sin will always draw a child of God away into the shadows. Sin will use multiplied diversions to redirect any attention from the sin. Sin will always bring more sin, such as lying, cheating, or stealing. Sin begins to reveal the character of Satan, which is no character at all. Jesus said about Satan:

John 10:10 (KJV) The thief cometh not, but for to steal, and to kill, and to destroy: I am come that they might have life, and that they might have it more abundantly.

Adam and his wife covered their nakedness with fig leaves and hid in the trees from God the Father.

Genesis 3:7 (KJV) And the eyes of them both were opened, and they knew that they were naked; and they sewed fig leaves together, and made themselves aprons.

It wasn't long before they heard God their Father walking in the garden in the cool of the day. Oh, how they used to love running to their Father to share with Him all they had done and discovered that day. God the Father would intently listen to all they reported asking questions and laughing with them, and asking them to show him more. Much like an earthly father would treat his children. Now, they hid from their Father, as they were crushed with condemnation over what they had done in the garden that day.

Satan will use temptation to lure a child of God into sin. Then when he has accomplished his goal of compromising a born again in Christ Jesus child of God, he will then use condemnation to multiply the bad feelings upon that child that has sinned. Condemnation is not of God. Romans chapter 8 states as follows.

Romans 8:1-2 (KJV) There is therefore now no condemnation to them which are in Christ Jesus, who walk not after the flesh, but after the Spirit. 2 For the law of the Spirit of life in Christ Jesus hath made me free from the law of sin and death.

So, a good litmus test of whether something is from Satan is to ask yourself if you feel condemnation. The Holy Spirit brings a conviction of sin but never condemns the person. Satan brings condemnation. For the child of God, there is always blessed forgiveness when one sins against the Father. Satan uses self-pity and condemnation to bring a greater level of destruction upon God's children.

Those in Christ Jesus have their sins forgiven and not just covered with the blood of a sacrificed animal as in the Old Testament, but washed away by the blood of Jesus! Literally, their sin is gone, and it is as if they have never sinned.

Genesis 3:8-9 (KJV) And they heard the voice of the LORD God walking in the garden in the cool of the day: and Adam and his wife hid themselves from the presence of the LORD God amongst the trees of the garden. 9 And the LORD God called unto Adam, and said unto him, Where art thou?

God's question of "Where art thou" was the Father wooing Adam and his wife to come and tell Him what they had done. This question was meant not for God the Father to find out where they were located, as God knows all things. God knew what they had done immediately upon their taking of the fruit and eating it. Of course, in their child-like nature, they were like the little child who has stolen a cookie from the cookie jar and adamantly denies it with chocolate cookie smeared all over his face. Their pronouncement of being naked alone revealed their sin to God the Father, for they had lost their innocence.

Genesis 3:10-11 (KJV) And he said, I heard thy voice in the garden, and I was afraid, because I was naked; and I hid myself. 11 And he said, Who told thee that thou wast naked? Hast thou eaten of the tree, whereof I commanded thee that thou shouldest not eat?

CHAPTER THIRTY
THE CURSE OF ADAM

I thought back to the earth where I had once dreamed of being caught at night outside in a suburban neighborhood naked and needing to find a way home without anyone seeing my nakedness. It was a terrible feeling of being exposed with nothing that I could do but hide from one bush or tree to the next, running to find a way to get home. I thought of that dream as I watched Adam and his wife's desperation after eating the peach from the Tree of Knowledge of Good and Evil. Their innocence and purity were taken by the snare. They were now caught in knowing that they disobeyed their Father. Now they were finding out what "death" really meant, and it was much more than just being extinguished from life. What they had known as life was now, in comparison, a living death. They were naked before their Father, and they could not hide from His eyes.

Here was an excellent opportunity for Adam to have repented to his Father, and one can only speculate how God, in His Mercy, would have responded. God can do wonders with a broken and contrite spirit. He is a faithful and merciful God. I thought of how Moses had asked to see God's Glory and how God passed before him and proclaimed in Exodus 34.

Exodus 34:6-7 (KJV) And the LORD passed by before him, and proclaimed, The LORD, The LORD God, merciful and gracious, longsuffering, and abundant in goodness and truth, 7 Keeping mercy for thousands, forgiving iniquity and transgression and sin, and that will by no means clear the guilty; visiting the iniquity of the fathers upon the children, and upon the children's children, unto the third and to the fourth generation.

Unfortunately, Adam chose another way. Instead of being broken and contrite to his Father and admitting what he had done with full acceptance of responsibility, Adam decided to blame the woman for what he had done.

Genesis 3:12 (KJV) And the man said, The woman whom thou gavest to be with me, she gave me of the tree, and I did eat.

Imagine how Adam's wife must have felt as she heard Adam blaming her. In truth, she was beguiled, but Adam knew better and was knowingly disobedient.

Now, it was the women's turn to accept responsibility and repent to the Lord for her actions with a broken and contrite spirit. Unfortunately, she chose to blame the serpent. She chose a path that is chosen by countless Christians that blame the devil for their sin, with the excuse "Satan made me do it!" Nothing could be farther from the truth!

Satan's only control over anyone is what that person gives him the ability to control. When one chooses or consents to go with Satan's temptation, they empower him giving him their will until they decide to withdraw their consent, cry out to Jesus for help and begin to resist. Satan comes with the temptation, and each person must decide if they will accept or decline what he is offering. For those who accept, there is always loss. Jesus said Satan came to steal, kill, and destroy.

John 10:10 (KJV) The thief cometh not, but for to steal, and to kill, and to destroy: I am come that they might have life, and that they might have it more abundantly.

One who chooses his way can be assured that they will have something stolen, they might lose their life, and they may be destroyed. The way of Jesus always brings life and life more abundantly. Also, the fear of the Lord is the beginning of wisdom.

Proverbs 1:7 (KJV) The fear of the LORD is the beginning of knowledge: but fools despise wisdom and instruction.

The fear of the Lord is often equated to "Honor of the Lord." Any parent knows the value of a child that honors them and is therefore obedient to their wishes over them.

The fear of the Lord would have kept Adam and his wife from falling.

Genesis 3:13 (KJV) And the LORD God said unto the woman, What is this that thou hast done? And the woman said, The serpent beguiled me, and I did eat.

Of course, Satan can never find a place of repentance. He is damned to eternal damnation in the lake of fire and will be tormented forever along with the angels who followed him and rebelled against God. So, God the Father never asked him what he had done but immediately proclaimed judgment against him and Adam and his wife. However, God also prophesied how He would deliver mankind from all Satan had stolen from mankind through the sin of Adam and his wife.

Genesis 3:14-15 (KJV) And the LORD God said unto the serpent, Because thou hast done this, thou art cursed above all cattle, and above every beast of the field; upon thy belly shalt thou go, and dust shalt thou eat all the days of thy life: 15 And I will put enmity between thee and the woman, and between thy seed and her seed; it shall bruise thy head, and thou shalt bruise his heel.

This prophecy was fulfilled by Jesus when He put Satan under His feet and crushed his head and when Satan bruised the heel of Jesus by the crucifixion. Archeologists have uncovered the skeleton of a crucified man from the time of Christ. The Romans drove the nail through the heel of His foot and not through the top of the foot. One cannot imagine the pain associated with such a thing. Anyone who has ever struck their heel against something and felt the unbearable pain that comes from striking one's heel can attest to how horrifying it must have been to have a nail driven through the heel.

God the Father then pronounced judgment upon Adam and his wife. This pronouncement was a judgment that Adam and his wife really brought upon themselves as they had been told by God the Father what the consequences would be if they ate of the Tree of Knowledge of Good and Evil. As to his wife, God said.

Genesis 3:16 (KJV) Unto the woman he said, I will greatly multiply thy sorrow and thy conception; in sorrow thou shalt bring forth children; and thy desire shall be to thy husband, and he shall rule over thee.

Before the fall of man, God created woman to be a helpmate to man. In that relationship of mutual respect and love, the man was not ruling over the woman. Instead, they existed together in a oneness that Adam and his wife never knew again. Many Christian marriages still exist with the "husband" ruling over his wife. When Jesus redeemed us from the curse of the law, He also redeemed us from the curse of the fall, meaning the original blessing bestowed upon Adam and his wife was restored. That blessing included the Adam-Adam oneness. One can always tell when a married couple is blessed with this restoration because they have a common bond and love that is Heavenly! As to Adam, God said.

Genesis 3:17-19 (KJV) And unto Adam he said, Because thou hast hearkened unto the voice of thy wife, and hast eaten of the tree, of which I commanded thee, saying, Thou shalt not eat of it: cursed is the ground for thy sake; in sorrow shalt thou eat of it all the days of thy life; 18 Thorns also and thistles shall it bring forth to thee; and thou shalt eat the herb of the field; 19 In the sweat of thy face shalt thou eat bread, till thou return unto the ground; for out of it wast thou taken: for dust thou art, and unto dust shalt thou return.

The man could not consider or understand the extent to which his sin had compromised his health and well-being. Before sin, Adam was clothed in the glory of God. It surrounded Adam and his wife like a force shield. Now, Adam and his wife's bodies were vulnerable to sickness, disease, and infirmity. Adam and his wife once had bodies that were almost invincible. Now, they had to suffer the death that had come into the earth. This curse included death to themselves and others, including all plants and animals. Even the ground was now cursed and produced thorns and thistles. Under the curse, all was working against Adam, and in sorrow, he now had to struggle to produce his living.

Visiting Matthew

After the fall of man, Adam, who had named all of the living creatures God had created; Adam, whom God had given an Adam-Adam relationship with his wife, called his wife Eve.

Genesis 3:20 (KJV) And Adam called his wife's name Eve; because she was the mother of all living.

God had to sacrifice the first animals to pay the price for Adam and Eve's sin. Sin always brought death, and the innocent animals had to pay the price. So, God sacrificed animals and clothed Adam and Eve with their skins.

Genesis 3:21 (KJV) Unto Adam also and to his wife did the LORD God make coats of skins, and clothed them.

Jesus redeemed us from the curse of the law and the curse of Adam. Those who can accept that redemption are no longer enslaved to the sorrow of working under the curse but have the glorious grace of living in the Kingdom of God on Earth. No longer is their ground cursed to bring forth thorns and thistles and the sweat of their face. In the Kingdom of God, there is the glorious grace of God's abundant provision and supply. Few Christians understand this redemption and, therefore, never enter the grace of the Kingdom of God on earth.

The first step of that redemption is to understand it and begin to proclaim the redemption. While on the Earth, as I worked on my property, I would curse any thorn and thistle as it was against the redemption that I now enjoyed living in the Kingdom of God. I would openly proclaim that my land was blessed and wholly set apart for my good pleasure, for it was my Father's good pleasure to give it to me. After doing this for several years, I noticed that fewer and fewer thorny vines would surface. The blessing was working in my life, and I had an obligation to proclaim it and believe it overshadowed my life!

CHAPTER THIRTY-ONE
THE TREE OF LIFE—JESUS

Sadly, God had to recognize that things could not be how they were before Adam and Eve took the forbidden fruit and sinned against Him. That sin had separated Adam and Eve from God and His glory, of which they were once clothed. Because God is Holy, Adam and Eve could no longer walk with Him and talk with Him in the cool of the day. There was now that separation that comes when one is not in a right relationship with God.

Adam and his wife chose to trust and obey a bodiless fallen angel rather than the beautiful and loving God that created them. God had proven Himself repeatedly that He was a caring, compassionate, nurturing, and loving God.

Of course, if Adam and Eve had genuinely repented of their sin, acknowledged their sin, and humbly submitted themselves to God, asking for His forgiveness, God would have quickly forgiven them. But they would still have crossed a line that effectively altered their communion with Him, for in their perfection, they had complete oneness with God. Those who are born again in Christ Jesus have that oneness with their Father restored to them and can walk through the garden of their life with their Father as Adam and his wife did before the fall.

Within the Garden of Eden, along with the Tree of Knowledge of Good and Evil, was the Tree of Life. The Tree of Life is a type and shadow of Jesus. Jesus is the only source of eternal life with God. Jesus said in John 14.

John 14:6 (KJV) Jesus saith unto him, I am the way, the truth, and the life: no man cometh unto the Father, but by me.

I thought about the earth and how many believe there are many ways to go to God. This doctrine is not Biblical. Too many find this out after leaving the earth for their eternal life, either in Heaven with God or in hell with Satan. God is Holy, and we cannot stand in the presence of a Holy God unless we are holy. Man does not have the capability of being good enough and thereby holy enough for Heaven. Men have tried self-righteousness since the beginning of time. It is impossible.

John 1:17 (KJV) For the law was given by Moses, but grace and truth came by Jesus Christ.

The law was given to show man that it is impossible for man to keep the law. In fact, the more a man tries to keep the law, the more he will fail. If that man ever breaks one law, he has sinned and will never be permitted to go to Heaven, for the wages of sin is death.

Romans 6:23 (KJV) For the wages of sin is death; but the gift of God is eternal life through Jesus Christ our Lord.

By death, the Word is speaking of being eternally separated from God, and the place where one lives for eternity outside of God is called hell. Only by the Holy Spirit of God can one walk in perfect righteousness with God. One cannot be filled with the Holy Spirit unless one is Holy, and Holiness can only come by one being born again in Christ Jesus. We first need to ask God to forgive our sins. Being washed spiritually by the blood of Jesus washes away our sins and puts our sins as far as the east is to the west from God's remembrance.

Psalms 103:12 (KJV) As far as the east is from the west, so far hath he removed our transgressions from us.

To fully understand this, consider that if one were to go north, eventually, one would bump into the south. However, if one were to go east, one would never bump into the west. So, it is when God forgives our sins. He remembers them no more.

Then the most remarkable thing happens: God's Holy Spirit comes to dwell with us, and we with Him! We are never alone but have the Holy Spirit of God within us, and that is the same Holy Spirit that descended upon our precious Lord Jesus when John baptized Him in the Jordan River. This indwelling presence can only happen because when one is born again into Christ Jesus, his sins are forgiven past, present, and future. In John 3:1-3, we read what Jesus told Nicodemus, a Pharisee that came to speak to Jesus in the night.

John 3:1-3 (KJV) There was a man of the Pharisees, named Nicodemus, a ruler of the Jews: 2 The same came to Jesus by night, and said unto him, Rabbi, we know that thou art a teacher come from God: for no man can do these miracles that thou doest, except God be with him. 3 Jesus answered and said unto him, Verily, verily, I say unto thee, Except a man be born again, he cannot see the kingdom of God.

After being born again, a person may look in the mirror and see the same older man or woman that was there before the born-again experience. However, they are not the same. They are uniquely different, for they are now holy and filled with the Holy Spirit.

Many in the body of Christ do not fully understand this miracle and insist on putting themselves under the yoke of the law to keep their salvation. This dependence on the law is a very slippery slope and always ends badly, for a man cannot receive his salvation by works or is he kept by works. A Christian who lives under the works of the law will grieve the Holy Spirit.

CHAPTER THIRTY-TWO
REDEEMED FROM THE CURSE

Genesis 3:22-24 (KJV) And the LORD God said, Behold, the man is become as one of us, to know good and evil: and now, lest he put forth his hand, and take also of the tree of life, and eat, and live for ever: 23 Therefore the LORD God sent him forth from the garden of Eden, to till the ground from whence he was taken. 24 So he drove out the man; and he placed at the east of the garden of Eden Cherubims, and a flaming sword which turned every way, to keep the way of the tree of life.

Jesus paid the price for our sins. He became a substitute for us so that we could have our relationship with God our Father redeemed and restored. Those that are born again have eternal life in Christ Jesus. When they die, they will go to Heaven and not hell. When God the Father looks upon one of His born-again Children, He sees the righteousness of Jesus, who died on the cross for that person's sins. That is why a born-again Christian is referred to as a saint. He may not be living like a saint, but he is a saint in God's eyes.

Getting one's name written in the Book of Life is a wonderful and joyous event. That happens when someone becomes a child of God by being born again in Christ Jesus. There is so much more that Christ did for us, and in a real sense, we live in Heaven on earth. Jesus Christ redeemed us not only from the curse of the law but the curse of Adam.

The curse of the law is spelled out in Deuteronomy 28:15-68. It records what Moses told the children of Israel that would happen if they chose not to keep the law. It essentially speaks to curses against their provision, ability to prosper by the work of their hands, ability to receive wealth, freedom from servitude, health, and life under oppression of an enemy occupation with fear and horrors. God gave them a very clear understanding of what it would be like to live in the blessing and what it would be like to live under the curse and suggested that they choose the blessing.

Jesus redeemed us from the curse of the law.

Galatians 3:13-14 (KJV) Christ hath redeemed us from the curse of the law, being made a curse for us: for it is written, Cursed is every one that hangeth on a tree: 14 That the blessing of Abraham might come on the Gentiles through Jesus Christ; that we might receive the promise of the Spirit through faith.

But to fully enter into the promises of God in Christ, a Christian must have faith in what Jesus Christ did for us and what He redeemed us from and take hold of that promise confessing it as their own. For example, a person cannot be saved unless he accepts in his heart and confesses with his mouth that Jesus died on the Cross for his sins.

Equally true, a person cannot be redeemed from sickness unless he accepts in his heart and confesses with his mouth that Christ redeemed him from sickness. A person cannot be redeemed from poverty unless he accepts in his heart that Christ redeemed us from poverty and confesses with his mouth that Christ redeemed him from poverty.

That same principle holds true to all the promises of God in Christ Jesus. If the curse of the law is debt and servitude, the Christian must believe that Jesus Christ redeemed us from debt and servitude and confess it with their mouth. One has to have faith in Jesus Christ to redeem them and be obedient to move in faith without wavering to receive the promise. Confessing it with their mouth is a confession among men that Jesus paid the price, and the curse has been redeemed. Therefore, a person must openly accept the gift of redemption for all of Heaven and earth to witness. Jesus said in Luke 6.

Luke 6:45 (KJV) A good man out of the good treasure of his heart bringeth forth that which is good; and an evil man out of the evil treasure of his heart bringeth forth that which is evil: for of the abundance of the heart his mouth speaketh.

Adam and Eve, when they sinned, let death enter humanity. They were both healthy specimens, and it took a good while for death to have its way with them. Adam lived for 930 years. The Word does not speak to how long Eve lived but presumably for close to the same period of time.

Eventually, sickness, disease, and infirmity made their way into the human genetic structure. When Jesus Christ redeemed us from the curse of the law, He also redeemed us from the curse of Adam. That is why Jesus is referred to in the Word as the Second Adam.

1 Corinthians 15:45 (KJV) And so it is written, The first man Adam was made a living soul; the last Adam was made a quickening spirit.

As Jesus defeated Satan on the Cross of Calvary, He utterly defeated him and took back the keys to death and hell.

Revelation 1:18 (KJV) I am he that liveth, and was dead; and, behold, I am alive for evermore, Amen; and have the keys of hell and of death.

The curse released on the earth when Adam and Eve sinned has been redeemed by Jesus Christ. Jesus has utterly defeated Satan! Like any redemption, saints must believe in their hearts and confess the redemption with their mouths.

The problem that most saints have is that they do not understand that they are the redeemed of the Lord. In their ignorance, they speak a curse over themselves, entering a relationship with many of the hardships they face in life by confessing over again the curse of Adam and the law.

John 8:36 (KJV) If the Son therefore shall make you free, ye shall be free indeed.

Like many saints, I made the same mistake when I was on the earth due to my own ignorance and way of life among men. However, as each truth of the redemption of Christ Jesus was revealed to me, I was able to get free and eventually entered a time of divine health. It was a glorious time in my life. I was learning about faith and walking in the promises of God. But I was overzealous and failed to realize when I did not have faith to stand for certain healing. Consequently, I waited too long to go to the doctor, which ended up taking my life.

With that thought, I found myself back at the podium in the crystal building in Heaven, and I was withdrawing my hand from the gold dome at the top of the podium. As I became aware of my surroundings once again, I saw Matthew standing next to Andrew. Matthew looked at me with compassion, "Are you okay, dad?" "I am okay," I said, "Just kind of hard to see it all happen right before your eyes and realize how much was lost." "It's all right, dad," Matthew said. "It is not an easy thing to see. But remember that Jesus redeemed us from all that was lost!" I thanked

Visiting Matthew

Andrew and Matthew, and I walked out of the time portal building through the revolving door and back onto the main street of Jerusalem.

CHAPTER THIRTY-THREE
A WALK THROUGH HEAVEN

Dad if you could meet anyone in Heaven, who would that be? Matthew asked. "Well, Matt," I responded, "I would love to meet Abraham Lincoln."

"Okay, we can do that," Matthew said with that twinkle in his eye.

We walked the Main Street of Jerusalem with the saints going here and there. They always with such joy on their faces with that youthful exuberance that life on the earth hammers away. Most would smile such beautiful smiles as we passed, and I felt such a oneness with them all smiling back and enjoying our walk. It was such joy to my heart to be alongside Matthew, and I thought of how difficult it was for my wife Mary, my daughter Kimberly, and me to go through our earth life without him. Now, I had the great blessing of sharing eternity with him, and soon Mary and Kimberly would also be with us.

As every day is in Heaven, this was such a beautiful day. Imagine the perfect fall or spring day on the earth. It's not too hot, not too cool; the sun is shining, the air is soft, green grass, trees, homes, buildings, and everything beautiful. Only in Heaven, there was no sun but only the light of the glory of God that lightened everything, bathing it and us in God's glory.

We were in the City of Jerusalem on the Holy Mountain of God. I cannot express in words how glorious it is. Words are insufficient. It was nothing short of a feeling of being raptured. How different it was from the evil I witnessed being unleashed in the Garden of Eden as Adam and Eve took of the forbidden fruit from the Tree of Knowledge of Good and Evil. How horrible evil is, and yet men are tempted by it. It was a mystery to me. Yet, on the earth, I had been tempted time and time again by the evil of the earth.

Matthew stopped in front of a particularly beautiful white house with a beautiful wrap-around porch. It had the appearance of homes I had seen in the south built in the 1800s. It was two stories, and on the front porch where rocking chairs. Sitting in two of the white rocking chairs was the Master with Abraham Lincoln to His left.

As Matthew and I walked up the sidewalk bordered by beautiful flowers, which were everywhere in Heaven, the Master rose from his rocking chair and approached us. As always, I fell at His feet in reverence to my God! Matthew was on his knees to my left. Jesus touched our heads, and we rose and embraced.

"John," Jesus said, "I understand that you would like to meet Abraham. He is so anxious to meet you too." I smiled. "Does he know me?" I asked. "John," Jesus responded, "There is a reason you were so drawn to Abraham Lincoln and his life while you were on the earth."

Indeed, Abraham Lincoln was one of my heroes. I had framed the Gettysburg Address on my office wall and had read just about everything I could get my hands on about his life and death.

One of the stories that fascinated me about the Gettysburg Address was that he had written it on the train to Gettysburg from Washington, D.C. He had resisted fully surrendering to Jesus up to that point in his life. He had known much suffering, having come up from the lowest economic circumstances, had taught himself the law, lost children, and had a wife with severe mental problems. Yet, he was profoundly affected by the suffering of others, especially those that bore the horrors of slavery in the south of the United States.

On that train ride, he finally surrendered all to Jesus. He then wrote the Gettysburg Address. Like so many of Abraham Lincoln's speeches, it was short and to the point, and it packed a punch. Most importantly, it was anointed. Lincoln had followed a long-winded statesman who had waxed broadly for two hours. Lincoln then stood up and delivered one of the most famous speeches of all time, taking just two and one-half minutes. The people were stunned. Time stood still.

CHAPTER THIRTY-FOUR
MEETING ABRAHAM LINCOLN

When I looked at Abraham Lincoln, he looked much like he did on earth before he had been elected president. He was tall and lanky, and he did not have the beard he wore at the time of his death. As with all the saints in Heaven, we hugged, and I felt the warmth of his love. He then hugged Matthew, and we pulled the rocking chairs together so that we half circled each other. Jesus was sitting in the white rocking chair to Abraham's right, and I took the chair to his left, and Matthew sat in the chair next to Jesus.

"John," Abraham said, "I watched your life on earth because you have a great love for people. That was the secret to my ministry on earth. I knew I was a politician. Therefore, I started out with a desire to obtain the presidency. But along the way, I found out that the Bible was the one book that I could read and meditate on that brought me into a place where I felt right about myself and my purpose in life."

"I had finally obtained the presidency, but it only came because I knew that God hated what the evil men were doing, owning slaves and treating them worse than animals. I saw the evil in it, and I knew I could not be silent about that evil. I had to speak out against it. I did so with reckless disregard for my own political goals. Surprisingly, I found that my message was well received by the multitudes, and I was elected president."

"Then, as evil has a habit of doing, the division began over the issue of slavery, and the South succeeded from the union, and the great civil war began. I could not let the union be divided, for it would have brought destruction to our great nation. War could not be avoided. My heart was broken by the suffering and loss of life that came over the issue of slavery. But right overcame wrong, good overcame evil, and the North ultimately won the battle. Evil then came and took my life, but what evil intended to do for evil only solidified the victory of good over evil."

"Mr. President," I began to speak, "No!" Abraham stopped me with his hand held up palm forward and said, "My greatest victory was surrendering all to Jesus on the day that I wrote the Gettysburg Address. I am Abraham for eternity, and the office I held belongs to the earth." "I am sorry for not understanding that fact," I quickly replied, "I was so drawn to you in life because I felt your great love for people. You boldly went forward to do what you believed was the right thing for the right reasons. You were one of my heroes."

"I appreciate your characterization of me being one of your heroes, John, and I can honestly tell you that I was one that was praying for you in life. That is part of the reason that you were so drawn to me and my life and ministry. But Jesus is my hero and always will be because of His great love and all He did in delivering me from death, hell, and the grave," Abraham said.

I looked at Jesus with tears in my eyes and said, "If it were not for Jesus, I would have never made it to the end. I was a walking train wreck before Jesus saved and delivered me. Jesus is and will always be my true hero," I said.

"May I ask you a delicate question," I asked. "I know what you are going to ask," Abraham said, "and it has been one of my greatest sorrows of which Jesus has wiped the tears from my eyes. No, my beloved Mary did not make it to

Heaven. She was born into wealth, and she wanted for nothing."

"I did my best to provide for her earthly needs but did little to provide for her spiritually. She was not mentally strong, and something happened when we lost our first son, Edward Baker. We called him Eddie. He is here with me in Heaven, as are all of my children. However, Mary never seemed to recover. She began to search out spiritualists, and she learned to read tarot cards and tried to comfort herself with having contact with our Eddie by means of evil."

"I knew better, but instead of confronting her with the truth of God's Word, I tried to play along and show her that the spiritualist and the tarot cards were not working. The truth of God's Word is "quick, powerful, and sharper than any two-edged sword, piercing even to the dividing asunder of soul and spirit, and the joint and marrow, and is a discerner of the thoughts and intents of the heart.""

Hebrews 4:12 (KJV) For the word of God is quick, and powerful, and sharper than any twoedged sword, piercing even to the dividing asunder of soul and spirit, and of the joints and marrow, and is a discerner of the thoughts and intents of the heart.

"I knew better, but I moved with fear because I did not believe she could receive the truth. So, Mary is not with me, and that is a reality I must bear. If I could have lived to see my second term completed, I know things would have been different. But truly, when our son, William Wallace, died during my first term, Mary was never the same. It put her over the edge, and she sought her comfort from darkness rather than the light."

"Abraham," I asked, "You said that you had watched my life from Heaven and that we were somehow connected.

How is that so?" "John," Abraham said, "When you were a younger man, did you ever have visions of wanting to attain public office?" "Yes, I did," I responded. "Did you ever have visions of wanting to be President?" Abraham asked. "Yes, I did," I replied. "But, I had so much bondage, and found myself beaten down."

"I never called you to carry all that," Jesus said. "I know, Lord. How much I know that now. I felt such anxiety about circumstances in my life and I knew it was not right. Things felt wrong to the very core of my being. My marriage failed, and when it ended twenty years later, it nearly took my life."

"You don't know how close it came to taking your life, John," Jesus said. "You had angels on assignment to keep you, and the years were tumultuous after that as you were extracted from the darkness you had "yoked up to" for twenty years," Jesus went on to say.

"I really didn't enter into the fullness of my ministry until 1995 when I surrendered all to Jesus," I said. "At that point, I had such a love in my heart for my fellow man, and I desired to serve. But I could never get things right when I ran for public office."

"I ran for public office and was defeated many times, but I had it in me to be president," Abraham said, "I had a vision, and I never gave up pursuing that vision. I had days of deep darkness when it seemed I was being swallowed up in the darkness. The closer I drew to Jesus, the more the darkness receded."

"In my first term, I would read His Word to keep me on a firm foundation. I could not have done it without being close to Jesus. My conviction over slavery was based on God's love that was shed abroad in my heart. I knew it was evil, and I felt God's righteous indignation against it and that I should do all that I could do to end the evil."

"I had the same testimony," I said, "I had never felt so right about anything as when I ran for public office. I loved every day of it, except the day after losing. After losing the second time, it seemed it was all I could do to hold my marriage together. My business began to fail, and my wife began to look upon me as a loser as she did not share my love for Jesus. She looked upon me as I had lost my mind as I was so fanatically in love with Jesus."

"It was at my lowest point that she left me," I continued. "I was devastated and felt so out of touch with who I was. It seemed that everything she thought and said about me was true. I felt totally defeated. Ever running for public office again seemed to be an impossible dream."

"There is always great warfare over those I have chosen to lead," Jesus said.

"That is why the darkness used to enshroud me," Abraham said, "It was so dark that if I did not have it in me to stand, I would have taken my own life. You were meant to lead your country John, and I was praying for you to overcome."

"That is why I was so drawn to your life and death," I responded. "You were drawn to me for a reason because I was to inspire you to go forward to take the ground of your own political life," Abraham said.

"Satan uses so many different things to divert my people from their true call," Jesus said. "You always accounted for the financial devastation of your divorce, yet you never realized how much you gave up by marrying outside my will."

"I called you to lead my people, and you became a caretaker of a house and yard for twenty years instead,"

Jesus said. I wept. "I am so sorry for missing your call, Lord Jesus!" I said. "All is forgiven, John," Jesus said. You became my servant and led many to know me. You had a higher call in my Kingdom."

I stood up and hugged Abraham Lincoln, and Jesus hugged him, as did Matthew. We then walked down the steps from his porch with Jesus walking with Matthew and me. I looked back and saw Abraham Lincoln sitting there in that rocking chair. He smiled and waved, and I waved back.

CHAPTER THIRTY-FIVE
THE GREAT BATTLE:
JESUS ASKS ME TO VISIT HELL

We walked together back to the main street in Heavenly Jerusalem. As we walked, I asked Jesus if it was Abraham Lincoln's appointed time to go home when he was assassinated. "No, John," Jesus said. Abraham Lincoln was my servant, and there was much I wanted to do for a young country founded on a love for me. The hatred that filled many against him was led by Satan who designed to take his life through the actions of John Wilkes Booth."

"Did John Wilkes Booth know you?" I asked Jesus. "He did not," Jesus responded. "I reached out to him throughout his life. He never heeded my beckoning. Satan used pride and hatred to bring him to the point of hatred toward Abraham Lincoln. He believed that he would be received as a hero in the South for his actions in taking Abraham Lincoln's life. All that Satan does is a lie. Instead, he was not viewed as the hero he expected, but only a man that killed the president."

"Abraham Lincoln loved me, and he loved others, including the people of the South. He wanted to heal the nation in that love and receive the South back with love like the father in the parable of the prodigal son. Satan had done his best to destroy the land that I was to use to send My Gospel out to the world. Now, he took the life of Abraham Lincoln to continue to disrupt and destroy the nation that I loved."

"I want my people to be free," Jesus continued and then said, "It is a great grieving to my heart to see the bondage of my people in the time that you lived. They are so shackled by the debt for the material things they covet. They live lives far above their means, and they know little of My peace because of it. They should be a people that are a living testimony of my love, peace, and abundant provision. Yet, they hardly have time to consider the losses due to their own bondage."

"Heaven and hell are real. Yet my people seem to spend their time meditating upon the world and what it can offer them, while the lost are damned to eternal suffering due to the apathy of my people. That is why I need you to go with me to see the horrors of hell, John. I will be with you the entire time you are there. You will be safe with me."

"Me, Lord?" I asked and said, "I don't want to leave Heaven and go to that place. Why would I have to go to hell with you, Lord?" "John," Jesus said, "I know how difficult it must be for you to receive this truth, but I have prepared you for such a time as this. You have seen the wonders of Heaven, and now I must show you the horrors of hell, for you are to carry the reality of both Heaven and hell to my people to awaken them from their sleep."

"Lord," I asked, "How can I do that from Heaven? My life on the earth is over, and you have brought me here to be with you and my family for eternity." "John," Jesus said, "I am asking you to go back for me and be a watchman to tell my people the truth."

"They will not believe me, Lord," I responded. "They already think I am peculiar, and when I tell them that you have anointed me to heal, they will look at me like I have a very active imagination."

"John," Jesus responded, "Some will believe you, and some will not. I will deal with each of my people when they come before me to account for their lives. Have you noticed that you have yet to go before the Father to account for your life?" Jesus asked.

"Yes, Lord," I responded. I was just talking to Matthew about that very thing, and I wondered why I was not brought before the Father." "John," Jesus said, "It is because I am going to ask you to go back to the earth and finish your call and destiny. Many will come to know me by the truth of what you tell them about Heaven and hell. Their souls need you to share the truth of my Gospel with them."

"Be it unto me, Lord, according to your will," I responded. "But may I ask you something?" I asked. "Of course, John," Jesus answered. "Hasn't my body already been prepared for burial?" "Well, John," Jesus said, "I can only say that there is going to be a miracle!"

We continued to walk, passing many of the saints who smiled at Jesus and us, but due to the respect for others in Heaven, no one approached us. Matthew, who had been privy to all that Jesus had spoken to me, looked at me and said, "Dad, you are one of the bravest servants of the Lord that I had ever known on the earth. I know it is hard to think about going back, but if you have a mission to complete, go and complete it and then we will be together again." "I love you, Matthew," I said. "You have always been a joy to me, even more so in Heaven because we have been so close. You are such a joy to my heart. I love you, Matthew." "I love you, too, dad."

"Okay, Jesus," I said, "show me what we need to do, and I will do it." "John," Jesus said, "I want you to return to your cabin to rest with your family. I will come again to you when it is time. Fear not! I will be with you." "Yes, Lord," I responded as we hugged. Then Jesus hugged Matthew, and I joined in a group hug of the three of us. What Glory! Matthew and I watched as Jesus walked from us and greeted several saints that now respectfully approached and hugged Him with their faces filled with the joy of the Lord!

We then walked on together, quietly contemplating all that Jesus had shared with us. Soon, we were walking up the path to our cabin. My mother and grandparents were sitting on the front porch swing smiling at us as we approached. Oh, what joy there was in Heaven! Joy unspeakable and full of glory!

CHAPTER THIRTY-SIX
MY THIRD PRAYER IN HEAVEN

I looked at my mother and grandparents and felt such love for them, knowing that my time was short. I did not want to say what the Lord had told me, nor was I sure that I could freely speak of that which was shared with me. How long would I have before I would have to return to the earth? I did not know, but for now, it was enough just to be in that glorious place where the presence of the Lord was everywhere, and His glory was shown about bathing us in His glory.

I walked up to the porch and hugged them. I felt such love for them and gladness that we were all together in Heaven for eternity. "What was it like being on the sidelines of all that happened in the Garden of Eden?" my mother asked, waiting for my response. "Mom," I responded, "it was enlightening to see how Satan beguiled them and tragic at the same time. How much was lost for mankind, yet I saw God's faithfulness and great love for us. The Father came quickly to bring them back to a place of grace. He spoke prophetically of the defeat of Satan and all that he had stolen from mankind."

My mother hugged me and said, "It will be all right, John. Our God is such an amazing and loving God. The battle will soon be over." "I know, Mom," I responded, "but it is a real battle for the souls of men, and we must never forget that fact until the last of the enemy is defeated and cast into the lake of fire."

I wandered upstairs and knelt at my bedside, praying. "Father, I thank you for your great love and all you have done for me. I thank you for Jesus and all that He is for us. I pray that I will be brave and strong to do all You have called me to do. I will go wherever You send me, and I will do all I can to accomplish what You have desired for me to do. I pray You may be glorified in all that I do." Then I heard the Father respond, "I have been glorified and will be glorified. You are my beloved son in whom I am well pleased."

I felt such love washing over me, and it was hard to feel anything but enraptured in that glorious presence of the Lord. I rose, lay on the bed, and closed my eyes, resting in His presence. I fell into a deep sleep, dreaming that I was in a hospital room.

CHAPTER THIRTY-SEVEN
A LOST SOUL HAS ONE LAST CHANCE FOR HEAVEN

I could see that there was a man in the hospital bed, and his family was surrounding the bed. They were all watching him, and I could tell that he was dying. He had a look of terror on his face, and his eyes were filled with that terror. His family looking on, seemed helpless to assist him.

I heard one of the men watching him say to a nurse who had come in to check his vital signs, "Can't you give him something to help him sleep?" "Sir," the nurse responded, "Doctor Snellingburger has ordered that he have no pain, and we have given him a shot of morphine just one hour ago. Let me contact the Doctor and see if we can up the dosage." "Please," I heard the man say to her with pleading eyes, "I don't want my dad to suffer."

The nurse turned and walked from the room. I saw another woman who appeared to be a patient at the hospital come into the room. She appeared to be in her late seventies or early eighties, and she was elegant in her appearance. Her hair was just so with a modern cut but colored with an honest grey. She had taken the time to put makeup on her face streaked with wrinkles of her life. Her hands showed her true age, bony and wrinkled with age spots and that thin skin look that most of that age have. Her eyes were blue, and she had a high forehead typical of those who carry a prophetic anointing.

She was walking with a walker with wheels on the front. I saw that she was balancing a Bible on the walker, holding it steady with her right hand. Although clearly suffering infirmity, this was a woman that held herself as a woman of means. Should there be any doubt, she had a gold bracelet dangling from her wrist, thick gold interspaced with diamonds. There was a large diamond engagement ring and gold wedding band on her wedding hand.

The man and other men and women looked at her with contempt in their eyes as she entered the room. "I don't mean to intrude, but do you mind if I have a prayer with your father?" The man looked over at one of the other women in the room, his eyes asking, and she was shaking her head in a body language for no. The other man and woman also waved their heads in the back-and-forth body language of no. "This is not really the best time," the man said, "would you mind? This situation is a private family moment." The woman with her Bible was unfazed by the denial. "Oh, I won't be but a moment. One little prayer won't hurt." She said, continuing to walk towards the bed.

Then a veil was lifted from my eyes, and I saw that two large angels of the Lord were with the woman. They stood twice as tall as she was and stood on either side of her, waiting and watching. Their presence made the woman that much bolder. I also saw that within the room were demons, dark shadowy creatures, and they had total control of each of the men and women surrounding the bed. There were other demons on either side of the man lying in bed, dying.

The woman pushed her way to the bedside and started praying a prayer over the man. "Heavenly Father, we come to you in Jesus' name!" At that name of Jesus, the demons binding the men and women and the man on the bed dying went berserk, and their agitation only created more turmoil in the people they were holding in bondage. I saw the two angels of the Lord raise swords to protect the woman they were assigned to defend. The man on the bed started to groan under the agitation.

The woman continued with her prayer, "and we lift this one before you Father as he is a son that needs to make a choice to go back to his Father. You are a good God, and You sent Your only begotten Son Jesus to die on the cross for all of our sins." Hear! The woman hesitated and said, "Sir, you don't have to go to your death not knowing Jesus. You can give your heart to Him right now and repent of all your sins, and He will wash away your sins by His blood that was shed for you to forgive your sins. All you have to do is accept the gift given to you. Will you accept the gift of your salvation now?" the woman asked.

It was at that moment that the demons joined together and began chanting, "No! No! No! No! No! No!" The agitation started to unsettle the men and women looking on. Their faces were anguished in disgust at the audacity of this woman coming in and disturbing their last moments with their father. The man who had spoken to the nurse started yelling, "you get out of here!" The man in the bed was agitated and began to shake his head from side to side. At that point, two nurses came into the room and spoke with the woman, "Ms. Dottie, come, we must go now. You are not welcome here in this room. Come on now." The man continued to yell, "Get her out of here!"

After the woman left the room, I noticed that the man on the bed was still agitated. One of the nurses returned with another shot of morphine. She inserted it into the I.V. line, and soon the man settled down, breathing shallow breaths. The other men and women continued to complain to the nurse about the intrusion that had just occurred. They vowed to make a complaint to the hospital administration with threats to include a complaint about the nurse whom they felt was lax in her due diligence allowing the woman to intrude.

CHAPTER THIRTY-EIGHT
WATCHING A LOST SOUL DIE

Hours seem to pass, and then I felt the Lord. As I looked to my left, Jesus was standing beside me. "Lord," I said, "You are here with me." "Did I not say that I would be with you always, even unto the end of the world?" "Yes, Lord," I responded.

The man in the bed and the other men and women in the room seemed totally oblivious to our presence. The men that appeared to be sons of the man in the bed were still watching their father, who was now struggling to take a breath. The two women, both dressed like women of means, were busy looking into their cell phones as if some great value would come to them in their search.

I saw the door open, and a doctor came into the room as the men moved back respectfully to allow him to enter. He checked the man with his stereoscope, opened each eye, and looked inside. He turned to the men and women and said, "I am sorry, but your father is in the final throes of death. It will not be long now. I will order one more shot to be given to him so that he will not be in any pain." "Thank you, doctor," the one son that seemed to lead the group spoke. The doctor left the room, and soon a nurse came back in and injected the morphine into the I.V. and respectfully left the room.

A few minutes passed. Jesus standing beside me, said, "Watch carefully now." "Yes, Lord," I responded. The man's breathing became even more laborious and shallow and then heavy and then shallow again. Then he stopped breathing. Each man looked at the other. The women looked up from their phones. Then the heart monitor began to beep a warning beep and then flat-lined.

A nurse entered the room and said, "I'm sorry, but your father has expired." The women began to feign crying, for it did not seem real, but both men appeared to be truly upset and cried tears of genuine sorrow at their father's passing.

Then I saw the man's spirit sit up from his body. Now, all the demons in the room looked at the man with glee on their faces. He looked around the room and saw his sons crying. When he saw the demons, he began to shake with fear. I could see the fear in his eyes, and it was genuine fear. Fear like I had never seen before in any human being's eyes. The demons were now laughing at him and his fear.

He proceeded to get out of the bed as he would have in his physical body, but his dead body still lay there on the hospital bed, motionless. He stood up and began to walk away from the room. "Where do you think you're going?" One of the demons said to him. The man said, "I'm going home. Leave me alone." "You're not going home. You are coming with us."

One of the demons then grabbed hold of the man's arm and three of the demons laughing with glee, began to escort the man away from the bed. The man had such a pitiful look of fear and anguish on his face. Looking back at his sons, he cried out to them, "Can't you help me?" They continued to look at his now dead body, oblivious to what was going on in the spiritual realm around them.

I then saw an angel of the Lord suddenly appear and block the path of the demons' holding the man in their grasp. The man could see the angel of the Lord, and he looked at him, hoping that he might be a savior to him in this moment of horror. The angel of the Lord held a Book in his hands, and he opened the Book, and with his finger, he traced down the page seeking to find if the man's name was written in the Book, but it could not be found. The man looked devastated, for he knew in his heart that would have to occur. He knew his name would not be written in that Book.

He had spent his life mocking the people whose names were written in the Book of Life. "What nonsense," He had said to countless people. He was a man of great success in life. Starting with nothing, he had amassed a fortune, and it wasn't anyone or anything but his own hard work and his willingness to do what it would take to win. He was considered ruthless in his business dealings, and he always came out on top. But he wasn't without a heart. He gave to a multitude of charities, served on many charitable boards, and had his name engraved on many a bronze plaque, and he was always one of the most significant contributors.

The angel closed the book and stepped out of the way, and the demons snatched the man up, and they went through the floor with the man now screaming for someone to help him. Jesus now took me alongside him, and we followed down, down, down into the earth we went. I saw the light of the earth recede, and it became so dark. Darkness like I had never known before. All the while, the man was screaming cries of anguish and fear. Soon, I saw a light appear from down below. It was a fire light like one would see dancing across the wall of a dark room with only a fire in the fireplace burning.

CHAPTER THIRTY-NINE
HELL APPEARS IN THE DARKNESS

As we descended, I could see we were coming upon the Gates of Hell. The demons dragging the poor man who had just died pulled him towards the gates while he resisted with everything he had within him. He kept looking back in the direction they had come descending into the darkness in hopes that somehow, he could get loose and find his way back out of that place. I will never forget the sheer look of terror he had in his eyes.

All of his resistance was for naught as the demons dragged him in through the gates and as he entered, the gates shut with the sound that the only thing I had ever heard that could come close was the sound of the jail cell door closing. Jesus and I followed along, seemingly invisible to those in the place of the damned. I stayed as close to Jesus as I could get. I felt fear all around me and deep penetrating darkness that was only broken by the flames in that place that shed an eerie light of their own.

Once inside the gates, the demons let go of the man, and he no longer resisted but submitted to his fate in that horrible place. I heard the screams of the damned constantly ringing out. The air and everything there was desert dry, and I found that I could feel the heat and the dryness making me thirst as I had never thirsted before. There was the rancid smell of death permeating everything there. It was the smell of rotting flesh.

Demons laughed and enjoyed the anguish that their victims suffered in hell. They laughed at the man that had just arrived. They ripped his clothes off, and he stood there naked and alone, so very alone. He cried out to God to help him, and he repented for turning himself away from God and his people. He begged God to give him one more chance, but there was only a dead silence except for the mocking of the demons, who laughed even harder at him at his cry for help.

They were experts in torture, and now they tortured the man with the remembrance of all the times that he could have accepted Jesus. In truth, they had deceived the man into denying Jesus each time he could have been saved. Now, they had got their prize, his soul, which they had stolen from God at the man's own choosing.

"You stupid fool," they chided with him, "don't you know you could have gone to Heaven if you had not denied that stupid woman who came to pray with you as you were on your stinking death bed. Just think you would have gone to Heaven! Wow! Heaven! But you held your place, didn't you? You didn't want any part of that Christian stuff."

The man looked like he was racked with anguish at the thought of how close he came to avoiding all this horror. Perhaps, he thought, I might still be forgiven, and he cried out even more, "Forgive me, God! Forgive me, Lord Jesus! Please! Please! Give me another chance." Again, there was a deadly silence.

Jesus turned and spoke to me, "How I chided and beckoned him to come to me. Even as a little child, I called to him. He was called to be a great evangelist for My Kingdom. Many would have come to know me through his call and destiny. But the enemy offered him the world and all that he had in the world. He sold his soul for great riches, the lust of the flesh, and the pride of life. How fleeting his temporal pleasures were for a season, and now he must face eternity without me." I was speechless as I watched this tragedy unfold before me.

Now, broken and without any hope, the man was led down a dry path. On either side of him were the damned in fiery pits lined with red hot coals as one would see in the bottom of a barbeque grill. The red hotness of the coals exuding heat and the poor damned soul stuck within the pit with no rest day or night screaming out in anguish at the flames and the unquenchable thirst. Both men and women were naked, and they had no thought of their nakedness as whatever pleasures they derived on earth by seeing such things were gone now in this place of torment.

The demons came to a particular pit that was unoccupied, and with a final shove, they pushed the man into the pit. He fell, rolling down the steep sides with the burning coals that lined the sides and the bottom. Jumping up to avoid the burning of the coals, the man grabbed at the sides of the pit, digging into the burning coals trying to climb out, only to fall back into the fire.

He screamed the cry of the damned. He wept, but there were no tears, for there were no tears in that place of dry heat. He kept crying to the Lord to save him, but there was no answer. There was but only suffering day and night and for eternity to follow. The demons laughed and laughed, enjoying every moment of the man's torture.

Jesus said to me, "there is no one here that did not get deceived into coming here by Satan and his fallen angels. They hate my Father and Me and do everything they can to hurt our heart by taking one of our children to this place for eternal separation from us."

"How horrible it must be for You and the Father," I commented to Jesus. "John," Jesus said, "You must understand that we do all we can do to keep all from coming to this place. But my Father and I honor choice. Every man and woman has the free choice to decide if they want to spend eternity with us in Heaven or eternity with Satan and his fallen angels. We will honor their choice."

CHAPTER FORTY
HELL: A PLACE OF SUFFERING FOR THE DAMNED

With that said, suddenly, Jesus allowed us to be seen by all. The glory of Jesus filled that place of the damned, and the demons that were just a moment ago laughing at the man all quieted and fell at Jesus' feet. I continued to stand beside Jesus as close as I could get and realized that I, too, could now be seen by all.

The man that had just died saw us standing near his pit and cried out, "Jesus, you came to save me!" Jesus looked at him in love and pity and said, "Son, you know how often I came to you and beckoned you to give your life to me." "I know," the man said, still crying, "and I am so sorry, Jesus, that I put off giving my life to you. I was going to do it, but something always came up, and I had too much going on that needed to be taken care of by me. I couldn't just drop everything because I had to take care of my business. But I will serve you now, Jesus. You just wait and see! I will serve you now!"

"Son," Jesus said, "it is too late. You should have made that choice in life. Now, judgment has been set. You cannot choose me now. You have made your choice, and it is irrevocable."

"No!" The man cried. "No, Jesus! Give me one more chance. Please just give me one more chance!"

"I cannot," Jesus said. "It is not for me to give. Your judgment has been set."

As Jesus spoke, I watched the man and saw that the realization of the spot he was in was finally sinking in, and he realized that he was not getting out of there. Then his pleading turned to hatred, and he began to curse Jesus and me saying vile, filthy things about us and cursing us with every bit of hate that he had within him. He seemed to have an inexhaustible supply of hatred and venom. Jesus turned and walked with me beside him, away from the man continuing to curse us.

"The truth is that even if he were given an opportunity to serve us, he would never be faithful, for he has always loved himself more than all. The love of my Father is not shed abroad in his heart." As we walked together, Jesus said, "When I died for you on the cross, I first descended to this place before ascending on the third day. I want to show you something."

As we walked together past thousands and thousands of the damned, it seemed that we once again had gone into anonymity as they appeared to be oblivious of us. Each of them, men and women, was in horrific suffering in the pits that had been prepared for them. I continued to feel the thirst and the heat as we walked, and it was as if Jesus allowed me to experience just a measure of the suffering the damned experienced. But it was the smell of that rancid death that was truly horrific. I felt like I was on the edge of vomiting from the smell.

We descended through layer after layer of the suffering damned, and as we descended, it seemed to me that it was even greater heat and suffering for those in the levels below. We passed one pit, and Jesus had us stop. He asked me, "Do you recognize this man?" I knew instantly, "Yes," I said, "Adolf Hitler!" "That's correct," Jesus responded.

The man I recognized as Hitler was just as I had seen time and again in pictures of the man. Now, in his agony and torment, his face in anguish, I could see his eyes dark and deadly. Satan tried to use this man to extinguish the Jewish race. However, his service to Satan earned him nothing more than a pit in hell in the burning fires for eternity. How ironic I thought that his reward was nothing but eternal death.

We continued to descend and stopped at a particular pit. It was empty but still had the burning coals within the recess and going up the sides of the pit. "Do you know why I am showing you this pit?" Jesus asked. "No, Lord," I responded, "why are you showing me this pit?" "It was the one that Satan had chosen for you, John!" Jesus said. "I was supposed to be here?" I asked. "Yes, John," Jesus said. "But I took your place and occupied it for you!"

"Oh Jesus, are you telling me this is where you were tormented for three days and nights after the crucifixion?" I asked. "Yes," Jesus said and continued to comment, "When I was placed here, Satan and his angels gathered around, and they had such glee at the prospect that they had defeated Me and had taken Me from my Father and had Me to torment day and night for eternity. Then on the third day, My Father's voice echoed through hell.

Matthew 3:17 (KJV) And lo a voice from heaven, saying, This is my beloved Son, in whom I am well pleased.

For it was prophesied by my son David in Psalm 86.

Psalms 86:12-13 (KJV) I will praise thee, O Lord my God, with all my heart: and I will glorify thy name for evermore. 13 For great is thy mercy toward me: and thou hast delivered my soul from the lowest hell.

"When My Father said, "This is my beloved Son, in whom I am well pleased," my Spirit and Soul still had "God-life," and all the demons and Satan himself bowed to me. They knew they had been had at that moment, and all their glee turned to sadness and sorrow. I took the keys of death, hell, and the grave from Satan and left him utterly defeated and powerless. I then ascended, and before I left the region of the damned, I stopped off at paradise. All the righteous saints saw it all, and they were all born-again. We left hell together parading before the gates of hell that no one had ever gotten out once coming to this place, and we ascended to Heaven to be with my Father."

With that being said, Jesus allowed both of us to be seen again. Once again, the demons bowed at His feet. Then I saw one that was a relatively small-looking man with a receding hairline who had dark hair and was clean-shaven. He was of small stature, but he held himself with pride, and I could tell that he was used to having his way. He kind of looked like Napoleon Bonaparte. He walked up to us and, bowing slightly, said, "Why have you come? Are you coming to torment us before the time?" "Satan," Jesus said, "I command you to be silent." At that, Satan said no more. I watched him earnestly, and he looked at me with eyes that penetrated. I could feel his seductions, but his eyes were dark and evil. They were pure unadulterated evil.

With that, Jesus and I turned and walked out. As we approached the gates, they began to open, and we walked through them. I was never so glad to be free of that place of suffering. The screams of the damned, the unquenchable thirst, the rancid smell of rotting flesh, and the dryness and heat were now behind me as we walked through the gates.

Suddenly, as the gates were closing, I felt a burning heat on my left arm and looked and saw that a demon had grabbed my arm and was pulling me back within the gates of hell. I cried out to Jesus, "Help! Help! Lord Jesus! Help

Me!" Jesus turned, and as the gates closed, the demon had me inside, and Jesus was outside. The demon dragged me into hell, away from the gates. I knew that I was being pulled into the region of the damned, and Jesus was getting farther and farther away from me as the demon dragged me deeper and deeper into hell. "Please, Jesus! I cried. Help me!"

At that cry, Jesus now spoke, "Cease and be still!" The demon stopped but still held me firmly. "What right do you have to take this little one?" Jesus asked the demon. The demon spoke in a strange language, but I seemed to understand what he was saying. "He is here, and that is my right."

Jesus looked at me and back at the demon. I was now encouraged by Jesus' presence, and I cried out, "No!" I command you to turn me loose in the name and blood of Jesus of whom I serve!" At that word, the demon turned me loose, and I ran towards the gates that were still locked shut. I reached the gates and said, "I command you to open in Jesus' Name!" The gates opened, and I walked out of hell and took my place alongside Jesus.

CHAPTER FORTY-ONE
MARY PRAYS FOR LIFE OVER MY EMBALMED BODY

We began to ascend through the darkness, and the light of the fires of hell, the screams of the damned, and the rancid smell of rotting flesh began to recede. The darkness became darker and darker, so much so that it seemed to have substance in itself. Then, I saw the light of the earth far above, and soon as we ascended, we came out of the pit into the sunlight of a beautiful day. We stood outside a funeral home. It was the one in which I had seen my wife and daughter speaking to the funeral director.

As we looked, I saw a car pull up, and it was my wife's car with my daughter driving. The vehicle was parked in the parking lot. I saw my wife and daughter get out and walk towards the door to the funeral home. Jesus and I followed along unseen, and I saw my wife and daughter waiting to speak with the funeral director. He exited his office and invited them in to sit with him.

"I want to see my husband, and I want to be alone with him." My wife spoke firmly to the funeral director. "Ms. Mary," he began to speak, putting on his most beguiling appearance of compassion. This request is highly unusual. May I ask why you want to see him alone?" "That is none of your business," my wife spoke back to him and said, "I want to see him. Are you going to take me to him, or will we need to remove him from your establishment?"

At this point, my daughter spoke up and tried to be a peacemaker, "Mom, why don't we go and let them be about what they need to do to prepare for tonight's viewing."

"No," my wife responded, "I am going to have some time alone with your father, and I will not take no for an answer!" The funeral director looked at my daughter and back at my wife and said, "Okay, give me just a moment to check on his progress and have everyone leave so you can have some time with him." The funeral director left the room with that, and my wife and daughter continued to sit there.

"Mom," my daughter said, "Please do not do anything weird in there. We have a service coming up in just a few hours, and I am sure they have got dad prepared for the viewing already." "I am not going to do anything weird!" My wife responded, a little upset at my daughter for her suggestion, "Unless you think praying for your dad is weird." "Mom," my daughter said, "Dad is in Heaven with Jesus. You don't need to pray for him in there. That is just his suitcase that held his spirit while he was here with us." "Do you think I don't know that?" My wife responded.

The funeral director then came into the office again and said, "Ms. Mary, we are ready for you to see your husband. He was already prepared for the service tonight, and I have brought his casket out of the freezer. He will be a little cold to the touch." My wife nodded and stood up and followed him to the back area of the funeral home where my body was kept. She had her Bible in her hands. My daughter followed, and my wife turned and said, "No, please wait for me." My daughter relented, although I could tell that she was uneasy with what was transpiring and wanted to go along to make sure my wife did not do anything out of the ordinary.

The funeral director opened the door to an area of the funeral home where family members seldom went. They entered a side room where they had a gurney with my casket on it. My body was dressed in one of my favorite suits as I lay in the coffin. "Take as long as you want, Ms. Mary, and I will be in my office with your daughter when you are done." My wife nodded, and the funeral director left the room, shutting the door behind him.

My wife stood there for just a moment, put her purse down on a chair, and began to pray. "I thank You, Jesus, that You redeemed us from death, hell, and the grave! Thank You that You have defeated Satan and that he has no place with us. We belong to You, Jesus. John belongs to you. You said in your Word in Matthew that You gave Your disciples authority.

Matthew 10:7-8 (KJV) And as ye go, preach, saying, The kingdom of heaven is at hand. 8 Heal the sick, cleanse the lepers, raise the dead, cast out devils: freely ye have received, freely give.

Jesus, John is Your disciple. He knows that You do mighty acts even now in Your Kingdom here on earth as a witness to a lost and dying world that You are the same yesterday, today, and forever. And now, Jesus, I pray that Your power will descend and bring John back to life. I believe and doubt not in my heart that You have the power to do this.

At this, my wife walked over to the casket, moving the chair closer, she opened the lower casket door, and I saw that they had put a pair of shoes on me that I wore with that particular suit. I had always wondered if they put shoes on the person lying in the casket since you could not see what was below. Now, I noticed that at least this funeral home did.

My wife then stepped on the chair, reached over with her right arm and leg, and crawled on top of me. Stretching her body out over mine, she put her face against my face and began to blow the breath of life in my face. Nothing happened. Then she began to say, "I speak life to you, John! In the Name and Blood of Jesus, I speak life to you. Live in Jesus' Name! Live in Jesus' Name! My wife was loud while praying, and I saw one of the funeral employees come into the room and start screaming, "Ma'am," you can't do that. Ma'am, you have to get down." The young man appeared to be in his late twenties, and he was beside himself at what he saw my wife doing. He got no response from my wife, who was continuing to pray over me, and he turned and hurried to the funeral director's office.

CHAPTER FORTY-TWO
RAISED FROM THE DEAD

At this point, Jesus looked at me and said, "It's time, son. I am sending you back. Write all you have seen and heard and let others know that Heaven and hell are real. Let them know that I will come quickly! Let them know that time is short, and they should repent and turn from their wicked ways, for I come quickly." "I love you, Lord!" I said and hugged Jesus tightly. "I don't want to leave, Lord." "I am right here with you, John. I will never leave you or depart from you. Even unto the end of the world."

At that word, I turned and walked towards the casket and slipped right back into my body. At that moment, the funeral director entered with his employee following and my daughter following behind them both. "Look here Ms. Mary. Get off of him! You can't do that!" My daughter looked shocked and said, "Mom, please, Mom." The funeral director grabbed my wife's arm and began to pull her off me. Mary was screaming, "Let me go! No! My husband lives!" As she was being pulled off me, I began to cough and sputter.

My wife got up on her knees. In a state of shock, the funeral director and his assistant helped her off me, and I sat up. As I did, the funeral director, thinking that it was some sort of bodily reflex that will sometimes occur in a dead body, began to push me back to a lying position. I opened my eyes and looked at him, and he jumped back. "What are you doing to me?" I asked.

"John," my wife screamed, "You are back!" My daughter ran to my side and said, "Dad, Oh Dad, you're okay. You are alive!" As I sat there in the casket, I said, "Can somebody help me out of here?" At this point, the funeral director and his assistant came back to the coffin and helped me out. I was still cold from being in the freezer, but my body was beginning to warm, but I shivered. "I am freezing. Does anybody have a cup of hot coffee?" My wife, Mary, and daughter hugged me, and I felt the shivering subside as they shared their body heat.

The funeral director said, "I don't know what just happened, but you are supposed to be dead. In fact, you are dead." "No, I'm not dead," I replied. "What just happened is that I was just raised from the dead." "That's impossible," the man said. "Nothing is impossible with Jesus," I replied. The man just looked at me.

"Listen," I said to him, "I know that you don't know Jesus." "How do you know that?" the man asked. "I know it because I saw you when you first met with my wife and daughter five days ago, and I saw then that you are not born again, and you have a demon spirit that binds you. It is a spirit of beguilement, and you beguile all that come through those doors acting as if you care when all you really care about is the money that comes to you from each funeral you direct."

"Now," I continued to say to him, "you have just seen my wife raise me from the dead in the Name of Jesus. Give your life to Jesus and repent of your sins. Choose to live for Jesus and not the devil." The man just looked at me and spoke. "I don't believe what I am seeing and hearing. I was hired to conduct a funeral. I did my part by doing everything I was supposed to do, including embalming you. You should not be talking to me."

"Will you give your life to Jesus right now?" I asked. "Let's get on our knees right here and pray a prayer of salvation." "Well," the funeral director said, "I'll give that some thought. But in the meantime, we have many people coming here for a viewing tonight and a graveside service tomorrow. What are we going to do about that?"

"I'll tell you what we will do," I said, "We will have a revival service tonight right here in this place, and I will greet the people when they arrive and preach the service." The funeral director looked at me, and I could see he was weighing the possibilities of all that had transpired and what he could do not to offend others that might affect business. He thought about the fact that this was a true miracle, and the people would be coming from far and wide to see the miracle of a man raised from the dead. And they would be coming to his funeral home. "Okay," he said, "You greet the people and lead the service."

With that concession, I turned and spoke to my wife and daughter and said, "Let's go grab a bite to eat before tonight's service. I am suddenly famished!"

CHAPTER FORTY-THREE
CELEBRATING JESUS AND LIFE AT THE FUNERAL HOME

That night at the viewing from six to eight, I made quite a stir as I stood by the door to the parlor with my wife and daughter beside me. People came in the door intending to pay their respects and stood in shock, looking at me. Some just simply turned and walked out, not knowing what to do. Most came forward and were genuinely pleased to see that I was alive and wanted to hear all the details. I promised to give my testimony in a short service to begin at seven.

I began the service by lifting up the Name of Jesus and telling all that I had died and what I had experienced upon leaving the earth. I shared how my wife never gave up and prayed to have me raised from the dead. I called for them to repent of their sins and give their lives to Jesus, who was soon to return. The presence of the Lord was mighty in that place, and people were weeping as I told of all that had transpired while I was gone and the reality of Heaven and hell. Many came forward and gave their lives to Jesus.

I watched the funeral director, and I could still see that devil lurking in the background still bound him, and even with the miracle of me being raised from the dead, he steadfastly refused to give his heart to Jesus. I thought of the damned in hell and their screams and cries and the horror of it all. This man had no idea what he was playing with in his stubborn refusal to submit himself to Jesus. Yet, it was a personal choice, and we had to acknowledge that all had the option to give their lives to Jesus or not. God would honor their choice.

Visiting Matthew

Just as Lucifer had a choice, Adam and his wife had a choice to obey or disobey, and they chose the way the devil offered and disobeyed their God and lost so much grace. Yet, our loving God immediately made a way of grace back for them to return to His communion. What a loving, compassionate God we serve.

That night after my service at the funeral home, I was once again able to go to bed in my own home with my wife beside me. I felt such wonder at all that I had gone through, and I dearly missed being in my beautiful home in Heaven with Matthew, my mother, and my grandparents. I knew that Heaven would be there waiting when I finished my course. I had much to do. I had a testimony that I wanted to share with the world.

Would people believe me? I knew that there would be some that would and some would not. It was not for me to control who accepted my testimony and who rejected it. My job was to tell them the truth. Jesus was coming soon! Repent and give their lives to Jesus. He said I come quickly. Jesus died so that no one would have to go to that terrible place called hell. He died to save them from death, hell, and the grave. In Him was life and life more abundantly than anything they had ever known. That was the Good News. The Gospel of Jesus Christ!

EPILOGUE

After reading "Visiting Matthew," you may realize that you have never had a personal experience with Jesus Christ. Maybe you have been a church-going person and consider yourself a good person for most of your life. Perhaps you have found your way into the dregs of life, having wallowed in the mire of the sin of addictions to drugs or sex. Maybe you have never been a church-going person, but you have lived a good life, and you believe that there is a God, but you have never personally come to know Him as your Lord and Savior. Maybe you are just tired and weary. Perhaps you have tried to find true peace and joy in the world, but it always leaves you sad and empty.

You can have a new start right now and a new beginning in your life with the assurance of your salvation. It is a choice that every man, woman, and child must make on their own. Nobody can do it for you. But, if you have never made that affirmative choice for Jesus, do it now. Say this prayer out loud and mean it with your whole heart. You are about to experience Heaven on earth!

But, before you pray the prayer, count the cost. You are about to become a citizen of the Kingdom of God on earth and in Heaven above. The demons of hell have been counting on you being theirs. They do not take losing well. Jesus will protect you but make sure you are not playing church. This decision is serious business to God. So, don't do it unless you mean it.

Jesus said in the Gospel of Luke.

Visiting Matthew

Luke 14:28-33 (KJV) For which of you, intending to build a tower, sitteth not down first, and counteth the cost, whether he have sufficient to finish it? 29 Lest haply, after he hath laid the foundation, and is not able to finish it, all that behold it begin to mock him, 30 Saying, This man began to build, and was not able to finish. 31 Or what king, going to make war against another king, sitteth not down first, and consulteth whether he be able with ten thousand to meet him that cometh against him with twenty thousand? 32 Or else, while the other is yet a great way off, he sendeth an ambassage, and desireth conditions of peace. 33 So likewise, whosoever he be of you that forsaketh not all that he hath, he cannot be my disciple.

"Father, I come before you in Jesus' Name. I am so sorry, Father, that I have not loved You first. I am sorry for loving myself and my own life above You. I am tired of living this way. I am tired of the sorrow and suffering and the darkness of this earth. I repent before You now for all of my sins, and from this point forward, I will live my life for You. I know that you are the True and Living God. I know that you sent Your only Begotten Son Jesus to die on the cross for my sins.

I believe and accept that Jesus came to this earth from You, Father. I believe that He was born of the Virgin Mary and is the Son of the Living God. I believe that he suffered under Pontius Pilate and was beaten so horribly that He hardly even looked like a man. I believe that He was crucified and died on the Cross for my sins. His Blood was shed for the forgiveness of my sins. He was placed in a tomb, and on the third day, He rose from the dead and ascended into Heaven, and from there, He will judge the quick and the dead.

I believe in the Holy Spirit, and I so want to be filled with your Holy Spirit. Fill me now, Father, with your Holy Spirit! Save me now, Jesus!

You gave Your life for me. I now give my life to You. Use my life for the benefit of Your kingdom here on earth and in Heaven above. From henceforth, I am living my life for You, Jesus. Give me a Holy boldness to proclaim to all the Truth of the Gospel of Jesus Christ. May I be your ambassador for whatever time I have left on this earth.

In Jesus' mighty Name, I pray!

Amen.

If you prayed that prayer out loud, I now pray over you.

"Father, fill this precious one with Your precious Holy Spirit. Fill them fully and overflowing as a witness to them now of their new birth in you. In Jesus' mighty Name, I pray. Amen.

There are five things that I would ask you to do now that you have been born again.

Tell five people today about your choice for Heaven and that you accepted Jesus into your heart and are living for Him.

Find a church that is a Bible-believing Spirit-filled church, and start hanging around mature Christians who will love you and help you. You can tell which church is the real deal by the presence of the Holy Spirit. If you do not feel the presence of the Holy Spirit, you are in the wrong place. Many religions are legalistic (they have many dos and don'ts and fill you with requirements to keep your salvation), and you will never feel the presence of the Lord in those places.

You are saved by grace, and it is only grace that will keep you. You can also go to church online until you find the right church for you. I would suggest Moore Life Ministries or Andrew Womack Ministries. Both of these ministries offer free teaching that you can download or stream. Each of these ministries is solid in the Lord and His Word.

Get a Bible such as a King James Version, New King James Version, or The Living Bible. I like the KJV only because it is much easier to memorize. The Holy Spirit will help you understand the Bible as you read it. Just ask Him to reveal to you what the Word means. Start reading the Bible in the New Testament and read the Gospels, starting with Matthew.

Spend time with Jesus every morning and every evening. I tell people to bookend their day with Jesus! I know that life is busy but make time to put Jesus first! Get up an hour earlier if necessary. Turn off the television a little earlier and spend some time with your Lord. You will be revitalized, and He will guide you in all things. He will keep you from much pain and suffering if you draw near to Him as He draws near to you.

Finally, get baptized as a witness to all that you have been born again. Baptism is not a requirement for your salvation, but it is essential as it represents the new birth as you are immersed and symbolically born again as you come forth from the water. It also is a sign to all, including our Father and His Beloved Son Jesus and His precious Holy Spirit, that you are not ashamed of Him! Jesus said in Mark.

Mark 8:38 (KJV) Whosoever therefore shall be ashamed of me and of my words in this adulterous and sinful generation; of him also shall the Son of man be ashamed, when he cometh in the glory of his Father with the holy angels.

You will find that your life will be significantly different for the better from this day forward. You spent a lot of years living outside of Jesus. Now, spend the rest of your life living in Christ Jesus.

Jesus is Lord, and God Bless you Always!

ABOUT THE AUTHOR

I have had a remarkably blessed life. Jesus protected me from an early age and set me apart for Him. I have wandered from his side only briefly and sought my own way with sorrows that followed. Born in Miami, Florida, in an unchurched home, I came to know about Jesus at a small Christian school I attended at the age of 10. I accepted Jesus as my Savior there but did not live for Him for the next 29 years.

I grew up in Miami, went to undergraduate college there, and was accepted into Law School at Florida State University and graduated in 1983. I have been a practicing lawyer for 39 years and have spent the last fourteen years as an Assistant State Attorney in Florida.

In 1995, a year of a great move of The Holy Spirit, I had a miraculous visitation of Jesus in my living room in Tallahassee, Florida. I was 38 years old at the time, just fixing to turn 39. As many who have had such events would testify, the visitation changed my life forever. I was instantly transformed and immersed in His Holy Spirit. I walked around for six months, bathed in the Anointing. After six months, the warfare began, and I walked it out with Jesus doing my best to be obedient to all He showed me.

In those first years after 1995, I had supernatural visions of Heaven and hell. I had visions of Jesus on the Cross and of Satan defeated. For thirteen years, I had tumultuous warfare and ended up losing all. I began a march out of the loss to the living once again in 2008. Seven years later, I was to celebrate my twentieth year of surrendering all to Jesus. I looked forward for two years to that time. It was going to be a glorious anniversary. As April of 2015 approached, I naively forgot that there would be someone else that had plans for my anniversary. It was someone that hated God and me.

On Friday, April 24, 1995, my son Matthew's life was taken suddenly in an automobile accident in Tallahassee, Florida. At the time he was dying, I was beside my wife Mary in our camper in Madison, Florida, and we were praying our morning prayers, oblivious to what was transpiring just sixty miles away.

I was told about Matthew's death at 10:30 a.m. that Friday morning by a law enforcement officer that came to my office, and time slowed to an agonizing crawl. That Friday night was the longest night of my life. I was cloaked with the Spirit of Death. I could not feel the Holy Spirit, and I could not hear God.

The following day, I cried out to Jesus to show me that Matthew was all right, and He reminded me of nine-year-old Matthew walking the aisle to receive Jesus into his heart in a little Methodist church we attended at the time. Jesus asked me, "Do you believe Matthew's name was written in the Book of Life?" Yes, Lord, I replied. "And it was not removed!" Jesus spoke. I was washed in the confirming witness of the Anointing of His Holy Spirit. The spirit of death that had cloaked me since hearing of Matthew's death left immediately, and the Anointing carried me through the days that followed.

Since that day, the Anointing has grown in my life and ministry. Jesus has called me to an Evangelistic Healing Ministry, and I have had the opportunity of praying over many that received Christ and were healed. All to His glory!

Four and one-half years after Matthew went to glory, the Holy Spirit gave me to write "Visiting Matthew." He has a purpose in all that He does, and I spent ninety glorious days visiting with Matthew in Heaven. It was healing to my heart and revealed to me the great battle for the souls of men.

My wife Mary and I live a simple life in Madison, Florida. We love Jesus and minister life and healing. As He leads, we follow. We are blessed with children and grandchildren and give Jesus all The Praise, Honor, and Glory for His Abundant Goodness, Compassion, Love, and Provision.

Made in USA - Kendallville, IN
47481_9781955830607
02.10.2023 1334